The Post-Industrial Prophets

Interpretations of Technology

the text of this book is printed on 100% recycled paper

N. A. Graham

THE POST-INDUSTRIAL PROPHETS

Interpretations of Technology

by

William Kuhns

HARPER COLOPHON BOOKS
Harper & Row, Publishers
New York, Evanston, San Francisco, London

To Christopher and Lois

A hardcover edition of this book was originally published in 1971 by Weybright and Talley, a division of the David McKay Company. It is here reprinted by arrangement.

First HARPER COLOPHON edition published 1973

STANDARD BOOK NUMBER: 06-090322-8

Contents

Acknowledgments

Grateful acknowledgments are made to the following for permission to reprint material:

The Clarendon Press, Oxford, for permission to quote from *Empire and Communications*, by H. A. Innis, 1950.

Doubleday & Company, Inc., for permission to quote from *The Hidden Dimension*, copyright © 1966 by Edward T. Hall, and *The Silent Language*, copyright © 1959 by Edward T. Hall.

Harcourt Brace Jovanovich, Inc., for permission to quote from *Technics and Civilization*, by Lewis Mumford.

Harvard University Press, for permission to quote from *Ramus: Method and the Decay of Dialogue*, by Walter Ong, S.J.

Houghton Mifflin Company, for permission to quote from *The Human Use of Human Beings*, by Norbert Wiener.

Kaiser Aluminum and Chemical Corporation for permission to quote from *The Dynamics of Change*, © 1967.

Alfred A. Knopf, Inc., for permission to quote from *The Technological Society*, copyright © 1964 by Alfred A. Knopf, Inc., and from *Propoganda*, by Jacques Ellul, copyright © 1965 by Alfred A. Knopf, Inc.

McGraw-Hill Book Company for permission to quote from *Understanding Media*, by Marshall McLuhan, copyright © 1964 by Marshall McLuhan.

MIT Press, for permission to quote from *Language, Thought and Reality*, by Benjamin Lee Whorf, copyright © 1956 by Massachusetts Institute of Technology.

Oxford University Press, for permission to quote from *Mechanization Takes Command*, by Siegfried Giedion.

Playboy Magazine, for permission to quote from "Playboy Interview: Marshall McLuhan," March, 1969.

Prentice-Hall, Inc., Englewood Cliffs, New Jersey, for permission to quote from the book *Ideas and Integrities*, by R. Buckminster Fuller, © 1963 by R. Buckminster Fuller.

University of Toronto Press, for permission to quote from *The Bias of Communication*, by Harold A. Innis, copyright 1951, University of Toronto Press; and from *The Gutenberg Galaxy*, by Marshall McLuhan, © 1962, University of Toronto Press.

Wayne State University Press, Detroit, for permission to quote from *The Technological Order*, edited by Carl Stover, copyright © 1963, Wayne State University Press.

R. Buckminster Fuller for permission to quote from *Utopia or Oblivion: The Prospects for Humanity* (New York: Bantam Books, 1969), *World Design Science Decade 1965-1975*, with John McHale (Carbondale, Ill.: World Resources Inventory, 1963), and the following books published by Southern Illinois University Press, Carbondale, Ill.: *No More Secondhand God and other writings* (1963), *Operating Manual for Spaceship Earth* (1969), and Robert W. Marks, *The Dymaxion World of Buckminster Fuller* (1960).

ONE

The Conduits of Change

Man rushes first to be saved by technology, then to be saved from it.

Gerald Sykes

Over a century ago Ralph Waldo Emerson commented dimly on the Industrial Revolution: "Things are in the saddle and ride mankind." A young nation, infatuated with expansive land, the vision of unlimited resources, and raw uses of power, was flinging railway tracks across the continent, building new factories, transforming its passion for the frontier into a technological dream.

The fears articulated by Emerson and others like him in that earliest splurge of technological power hardly slowed the forces at work. Gradually, as historians like Mumford and Giedion have shown, America gave industry everything it needed to thrive: a sympathetic economic system, a period of inventiveness perhaps never before equaled in history, room to grow, and a cheerful willingness to adapt, within limits, to the requirements of new industries. By the turn of the century technology had become as deeply imbedded in the American mind as any of the earlier ideals. Indeed, technology seemed to know no boundaries. But that hardly mattered. The dream of creating a civilization powered by the machine, freeing man from labor, and uniting the vast continent was enough to build a new empire.

Today we are faced with the scale, the power, and the thrust of that empire, and dark suspicions have formed. Norman Mailer questions whether we haven't somewhere lost our soul to the whore of technology. Jacques Ellul sees the primal force of technology—technique—at work in every recess of the culture, gradually shaping man into its own image, the technician. Lewis Mumford, who once looked to an aesthetic of the machine as the bridge between the mechanical and the humanistic, more recently has claimed that we are lunging forward in a locomotive that gathers speed daily, but that has no engineer and no brakes.

Indeed, criticism of technology and the claims it has made upon our culture is no longer the sole province of literati, intellectuals, and romantics. A major designer of the science of cybernetics, Norbert Wiener, has voiced large doubts about the future of the computer. A generation of young people has sought some alternative to the society that they feel has become a megalithic machine, stamping, pressing, and manipulating men to fit them for its organizational cogs.

But the most frequent and perhaps the most valid doubts about technology stem from the world it has shaped. As our waterways become sewage pits and the air fills with poisons, the technological utopia that has guided the American dream seems to have been grotesquely inverted. A battered landscape of eroded soil, broken bottles, and automobile tires tells another story of technology from that dream of a thriving industrial world set within a barely tamed wilderness that spurred on our ancestors.

What has gone wrong? Is it fair to blame technology for our ecological crisis, or has technology been nothing more, as the conventional wisdom goes, than the tools by which greedy and insensitive men have plundered the environment? To put the question on another footing, is technology totally within man's control?

To judge from history, one might say that technologies are within man's control, but that their consequences are not. When the automobile appeared at the turn of the century, it gradually displaced the horse and carriage, and in ways that suggested that it was little more than a horseless carriage. But the automobile, with its faster speed, its considerably wider ambits, and its different requirements, gave it the power to modify social and urban patterns that the horse and carriage never would have touched. The automobile changed the city from the pedestrian scale to its own automotive scale. It created suburbs and the new patterns of commerce represented by shopping centers. It has changed sexual mores, the process of growing up, and a range of other cultural and personal experiences.

In his book *Future Shock,* Alvin Toffler has claimed that we are being accelerated into the future at such a rate that we cannot really adapt to the changes. Seen from another perspective, the problem becomes one of identifying and even learning to predict the process by which new technologies transform our lives. Toffler admits that we have only vague ideas of just what the implications of a new technology will be when it is introduced into society. When the early engineers perfected the selenium tube to make television possible, who could have anticipated the fact that nearly a hundred million people would spend more waking hours watching television than engaging in any other activity? If the historians of technology have shown anything, it is that new technologies are filled with surprises.

Systematic efforts to map the channels of technological change have generally been unsuccessful. Possibly the most impressive is that of Harold Adams Innis, McLuhan's teacher in media theory, who observed that a new medium tends to reorganize the movement of information within a society and thus create new sources of power. Lewis Mumford has pointed out another method, looking to the sources of power, such as air or coal or electricity, and the dominant material, such as wood or plastic, as keys to the cultural changes precipitated by new technologies within different eras.

Yet we are faced before the end of the century with the prospect of technologies that outscale anything we have witnessed in the past. What changes can be interpolated from the biological revolution of memory drugs, genetic engineering, and plastic organs? Laser holography promises a form of television in which images will be three dimensional: perhaps someday as defined and as convincing as real objects. The introduction of computers can already be felt in business, government, and education; what will be the implications of the availability of a compact computer monitor for virtually everyone in the society?

The ecologists have provided a helpful frame of reference for the problem. In an ecosystem, such as a large valley, the introduction of any new organism, change in the landscape, or alteration of the weather creates a fresh factor that alters the system. A natural landslide, for example, might destroy the breeding place of rattlesnakes, forcing them deeper into the valley floor, and requiring them to change their diet from field rodents to baby birds. If the ecosystem is diverse and healthy enough, it can adapt to the change without too great a loss—perhaps only the disappearance of that species of bird from the valley and a higher population of field rodents. By studying an ecosystem, particularly over a span of years and throughout a variety of changes, ecologists are able to calculate the probable effects of specific changes and the introduction of new elements into the system. Not that the ecologists don't encounter surprises. The discovery that the phosphates from laundry pre-conditioners lead to rampant algae and asphyxiation of the fish in streams was unexpected by all but a few ecologists. Yet the ecological conceptions of systems, of biological and chemical interplay between species, and particularly of the probable outcome of specific changes provide a badly needed model by which we can begin to locate and map the conduits of technological change.

But there is more to technological change than the conduits by which it affects a culture. What are the dimensions of the changes brought about by new technologies? Are the changes apparent and available to empirical studies, as the shape of cities after the automobile? Or do they tend, through their environmental presence, to be so omnipresent as to be invisible? In the 1920s, T. S. Eliot noted that the automobile had transformed man's experience of rhythms. The work of Marshall McLuhan and Harold Innis suggests that the changes brought about by new media affect societies so thoroughly and yet so unnoticably that these changes are almost impossible to detect.

Indeed, it seems one of the more striking problems raised by technology that we have no idea what limits, if any, exist to the modifications in our lives created by the new environments. Man, contrary to Mr. Toffler, is an incredibly adaptable creature: capable of sustaining subzero Arctic winds, the torrid humidity of the tropics, even, with the help of technology, the vast emptiness of space. But our very adaptability makes the problem of assessing to what degree we have adapted to new conditions all the more difficult. We are in the position of creatures on the valley floor who may know something is happening to their comfortable cycle of life, but can't be sure what it is. Our best clues, and historians like Mumford and Innis have used them well, are the institutions and practices that have survived from older periods and now exist, like earlier geological strata, alongside the newer institutions and activities that recent technologies have fostered.

A basic problem, one that is dealt with too infrequently, is defining what is meant by technology and, subsequently, by technological change. It is easy enough to see that a laser represents a new technology: but does a sophisticated method of sensitizing group members to one another constitute a technology in any valid sense? Ellul would say so; indeed, one of the most remarkable features of his thesis is a definition of technology (technique) that reaches far beyond the "hardware" of machines and electronic devices—suggesting that technology is not so much a phenomenon of energy transformation or work or even applied science, but a way of doing things and a way of thinking about doing things—a state of mind and being.

Dealing within a more limited framework, the concept of the machine, Lewis Mumford has provided another frame of reference from which to judge the nature of technology. He speaks of the immense organizations of slaves who constructed the pyramids as megamachines: machines that comprised men as their moving parts. His argument, set forth in *The Myth of the Machine*, is convincing and important: it enables us to think of the machine in terms of its structural and work-accomplishing features. Whether a machine is constructed from steel, plastic, wood, or human slaves matters less than what work it does, how it has appeared in a culture, and what impact it makes upon the culture.

Related to the definition of technology is the concept of overlapping technologies. Mumford has pointed out three major phases in technological history, separated on the basis of their power sources and dominant materials: the eotechnic (water and air power, wood and glass); the paleotechnic (coal and steam power, iron) and the neotechnic (electric power and the lighter alloys and plastics). While Mumford uses the same method to interpret each phase, he argues that the power source and the familiar material of a phase defines that age and significantly shapes the cultural experience for the people of that age.

Here Harold Innis and Marshall McLuhan go further by positing a different theory of overlapping technologies. By concentrating on media as the most significant technologies of any period—they both assume that information movement does more to modify a culture than the uses of energy or materials—they have each come up with different theories of interacting and overlapping technologies. For Innis, a new medium tends both to subvert and offset the power establishment and cultural bias maintained by the previous medium. New media relate to the older media like a pendulum relates to its latest swing—by a reversal or a lunge in the opposite direction. For McLuhan, a new medium uses the previous medium as its content, so that the content of television becomes movies, just as the content of movies has been novels and plays. Both Innis and McLuhan argue for a theory of change among technologies in which some decisive causal relationship exists between an older and a newer technology.

In terms of our present situation, such an idea is particularly valuable because it enables us to observe how the mechanized technologies of the nineteenth century have interacted with the electronic technologies of the twentieth. Perhaps more helpful is the method it gives us for anticipating the interrelationship between electronic (and even mechanical) technologies and coming developments such as genetic engineering.

The greatest contribution of Innis and McLuhan, however, may well lie in pointing out the central factor of information movement and control within older and particularly more recent technologies. Until recently we have thought of information technologies, from the printing press to the telephone, as communication technologies. Innis and McLuhan suggest a different understanding. These are only the more obvious information technologies: what of the computer, of automation, of coming developments like genetic control? The notion of information movement and control as the underlying basis of our most developed technologies is important. Whereas people of the nineteenth and early twentieth centuries identified technology with the work-performing, energy-transforming machine, we are learning to identify technology with media and other forms of information control.

The distinction between a machine-dominated, or mechanistic interpretation of technology, and an information-control interpretation leads to major new considerations. The most important of these is the way in which one conceives technology in relationship to man. The rationalists of the eighteenth century used the machine as a model by which they attempted to understand the universe and man: all of nature was seen as a mighty clockwork, and the role of science was to learn the workings of its gears. In the nineteenth and early twentieth centuries the most antagonistic critics of technology, from Samuel Butler to D. H. Lawrence, aimed their most virulent attacks directly at the machine. The machine was interpreted as a principle of its own, opposed to man; and most critics saw its action as that of imposing its own mechanized patterns upon man, degrading and dehumanizing him even as it made him increasingly into its own image. Charles Chaplin's *Modern Times* (1934) depicts a worker on an assembly line who, after work is over, cannot break out of the mechanized arm and leg movements that he has been making all day.

The theorists represented in Part I, under the heading "In the Shadow of the Machine," each represent some aspect of this interpretation of technology and technological change. Lewis Mumford, while more historically analytical in his *Technics and Civilization* (1934) than censorious, maintains some ambivalence toward the machine. His later works, however, particularly *The Myth of the Machine* (1968), question the accomplishment of the machine and particularly man's belief in it. Siegfried Giedion's historical study of mechanization is almost a scholar's counterpart to the story of what happens to the Chaplin's assembly-line worker in *Modern Times*. Jacques Ellul's *The Technological Society* (1954) goes beyond the machine, but takes mechanical technology as its model: no one, except perhaps the anti-utopians, has given such a grim depiction of our situation.

Harold Innis and Marshall McLuhan, focusing on media, have taken a different starting point and a different route, and have reached unique conclusions about man's relationship to technology. Where the mechanized conception of technology led almost inevitably to a polarization of man and machine, the media or information-control interpretation leads to a conception of organic continuity between man and his technologies. This conception is latent in Innis, visible mainly through his entangled view of history. But it becomes pronounced in McLuhan, who considers all media "extensions of man" and who likewise considers most modern technologies, from the automobile to the electric light, extensions of media.

A principle of organic continuity between man and his technologies not only posits a new harmony, but provides an entirely different set of values by which man can judge his technologies and their effects. Virtually all the men in this volume claim in some way that technology is not morally neutral, but beyond this they differ sharply. Mumford places the blame for our situation upon the blind uses of technological power in recent centuries, particularly our own. Ellul claims that technique has a near-diabolic life force of its own, and that man is virtually helpless to curb or stop it. In other words, Mumford places the values within technology but the blame goes to the men who controlled it; Ellul is more like a man watching a disaster so enormous that blame is a pointless luxury; he places the values within technology, but considers man powerless to affect these values—or technology. Giedion, who makes few judgments, preferring rather to follow the historical processes, would fall between the two positions, perhaps slightly closer to Ellul.

For Innis and McLuhan, who see the process of technological change as an almost necessary historical and ecological development, questions of blame and value have no meaning. This approach comes less from a happy faith in technology than a method of inquiry that leaves value questions out of consideration. The problem of value judgments, as both Innis and McLuhan have observed, is that they tend to appear before rather than after a study, and invariably create a kind of tropism toward the desired conclusions. Both men have their own biases, to be sure—for example, the preference for oral over printed media—but these biases are not value judgments in the same way that those of Mumford, Giedion, and Ellul are.

The men described in Part III, "Vortices of the New Ecology," represent the phalanx of engineers, planners, and systems designers who are reshaping our environment with the aid of electronic technologies. Their assumptions and their work transcend the problem of the machine, simply because they are no longer limited to mechanized technologies. Robert Boguslaw has described these men as "the new utopians"—they intend nothing less than a rescaling of our world into an automated utopia.

This young tradition of theorists, represented most vividly by Buckminster Fuller, tends, like Innis and McLuhan, to work outside the pale of value judgments. The title of Fuller's sophisticated, computer-guided game describes their ultimate desire well: *Making the World Work*. To be sure, there are values deeply imbedded in their activities and designs: values of efficiency, organization, collaboration, and precision, for example. But the larger questions of humane, spontaneously organized environment as against a pre-planned environment are beginning to take shape among these men only slowly.

The purpose of this book is to examine these three traditions of thought and describe the most important questions raised by each of the men included. It would distort the enormous differences in their background and their work to consider all of them, from Mumford through to Ellul, as a single tradition in any but the most expanded sense of the word. However, each of these men has dealt with the questions central to our time. What is technology? What are the routes of technological change? What, if any, are the boundaries of technological change? Is there a principle of determinism inherent in the impact technology makes upon a culture, and if so, what? How can we evaluate the significance of an old, a new, or even a future, technology?

PART I

In the Shadow of the Machine

TWO

Golem Awakens

> I have heard my teacher say that whoever uses machines does all his work like a machine. He who does his work like a machine grows a heart like a machine, and he who carries the heart of a machine in his breast loses his simplicity. He who has lost his simplicity becomes unsure in the strivings of his soul. Uncertainty in the strivings of the soul is something which does not agree with honest sense. It is not that I do not know of such things; I am ashamed to use them.
>
> The ancient Chinese sage,
> Chuang-tzu, quoted in Werner Heisenberg's
> *The Physicist's Conception of Nature*

The medieval legend of the Golem tells of the Rabbi of Prague who molds a statue of clay, and placing the unspoken name of the Almighty on its forehead, gives it life. The Golem grows, stretching in size and in weight and in the ability to perform great tasks. Once the townspeople begin to fear it, they erase the first letter of the name on its forehead, stilling it forever.

As Mumford and Ellul—and to some degree Giedion—would have it, Golem *has* reawakened. His footsteps echo in factories, in the reverberations of new household commodities, in the rotating gears of every watch. The man of flesh may yet perish at the onslaught of the man of clay. Such is the power of Golem, or his modern equivalent, the machine.

We live in the shadow of the machine, these men suggest, and that darkness may spell the doom of civilization. The fear is not peculiar to the twentieth century; its echoes reach us from Emerson and Thoreau, from Samuel Butler and Matthew Arnold. "It is the age of machinery," Thomas Carlyle stated in *Signs of the Times*. And Samuel Butler, in the essay that formed the basis for "The Book of the Machines" in *Erewhon*, "We are daily giving them [the machines] greater power. . . . In the course of ages we shall find ourselves the inferior race." Long before the computer, men feared the recklessness of power that could shape machines who would threaten, perhaps replace, men. Consider the Greek myth of Pygmalion, Mary Shelley's *Frankenstein*, Karel Čapek's *R.U.R.*

The dominant tradition of thought in literature, popular fiction, and science fiction regards the machine as an enemy. In his anthology *Of Men and Machines,* Arthur O. Lewis, Jr., has gathered an impressive collection of essays, poems, and fiction from this tradition: suggesting not only its range, but as well its common fear—that in displacing man, the machine will somehow destroy him. "Considered from the modern technical point of view," writes the sociologist Robert Jungk, "man is a useless appendage."

Seldom has the modern fear of the machine been articulated as well as in Čapek's well-known play *R.U.R.* Written shortly after World War I, it depicts the last days of man and the beginning of the new race. The setting is an unnamed island in some undated future, where Domin, general manager of Rossum's Universal Robots (R. U. R.), works with a small handful of man and thousands of robots to make production of the intelligent, work-hardy robots meet the demand. The initial material for robot life—an alternative to protoplasm—had been discovered long ago by Rossum and was given shape and substance by his son, an engineer. Old Rossum had wanted to create man for what Domin calls "atheistic" reasons: "He wanted to become a sort of scientific substitute for God. He was a fearful materialist, and that's why he did it all. His sole purpose was nothing more nor less than to prove that God was no longer necessary." Young Domin, however, has only a technician's interest in devising a robot:

DOMIN. Have you ever seen what a Robot looks like inside?

HELENA. No.

DOMIN. Very neat, very simple. Really, a beautiful piece of work. Not much in it, but everything in flawless order. The product of an engineer is technically at a higher pitch of perfection than a product of nature.

Rossum's men are constantly improving their product, and it is not too long before rumblings of revolt reach them from Europe. Already human births have ceased; apparently no one feels the need any longer for more people. When revolt finally reaches the island, Domin and his cohorts hope to stave off their own destruction by bargaining with the robots—their lives for the formula that is the robots' only hope for survival. But in a desperate play against fate, Domin's wife burns the formula. In the epilogue the sole human survivor, an aged scientist, bends over his book and formulas—in all these years he has not been able to repeat Rossum's formula for shaping robots, and he doubts that he can. He needs live robots for anatomical experiments, and when the affections between a pseudo-male and pseudo-female robot interfere, he suddenly recognizes that the problem, and the future of the earth, has been taken out of his hands. "Go, Adam," he says to them, "go, Eve; the future of the world is yours."

Despite its apodictic thrust, *R.U.R.* presents a cogent interpretation of several levels of relationship between man and the machine. What begins as an impulse to displace God leads to the technical effort to triumph over nature—and in that triumph is the ultimate defeat of the race. The idea that intelligent machines will take over the earth has been suggested elsewhere (both Norbert Wiener and Arthur C. Clarke have proposed the theory of evolution that *R.U.R.* depicts), but we find the suggestion chilling. The very reason why robots should *not* inherit the earth is because they lack the emotions, or as Domin puts it, the "bit of madness," that gives man his uniqueness and his belief in a soul.

Čapek has said elsewhere, "The conception of the human brain has at last escaped from the control of human minds." The machine is not only a means for doing work more efficiently and at less human cost; it also becomes an imposition between man and the world around him or, in the event of robots, between man and his own brain. The robots' elimination of work leads to the elimination of man—not because man cannot live successfully with the machines (an alternative inconceivable to Domin and his scientists and managers, though quite obvious to Domin's wife), but because the very principle by which machines impose themselves between man and the world *blinds* man to the dangers and excesses implicit in using machines. Technology can be as much a fever as a benefit, Čapek suggests (as do Mumford, Giedion, and Ellul), but we may not recognize the symptoms until much too late.

Čapek's play is constructed on a premise common among the men featured in this section: that the machine represents a principle alien to man and therefore destructive to him. Hallemeier, one of R.U.R.'s enthusiastic scientists, articulates the law of the timetable: "If the timetable holds good, human laws hold good; divine laws hold good; the laws of the universe hold good; everything holds good that ought to hold good. The timetable is more significant than the gospel; more than Homer, more than the whole of Kant. The timetable is the most perfect product of the human mind." Timetables are the proficiency of robots, however, not men.

The word *machine* originated from the Greek *mekhos*—a means or an expedient. Ellul's concept of "technique" interprets the machine strictly as the source of an all-pervasive technical consciousness; men need not fear the machine, but the degree to which their lives become modeled upon its organization, efficiency, rhythm, and principle of utilization. Mumford shows that the introduction of new machines has acted upon Western culture like geological shifts over a terrain, constantly changing the landmarks but ultimately weakening the original fabric. Giedion's study of mechanization reveals the distinct processes whereby the modern experience of time and space became dominated by the characteristics of machine efficiency.

Mumford and Giedion approach the machine historically; Ellul, philosophically. All three have noted in common distinct characteristics about the way in which machines transform a culture. For example, new machines are introduced as useful tools, but eventually they become absolutely necessary to the economic and social fabric—until they are replaced by more sophisticated machines. Likewise, no machine acts alone. Don Fabun describes today's technology as a complex of "machine systems." The washing machine depends on electric current and water flowing at a certain pressure; these in turn depend upon dynamos, circuitry, pumps, a range of various machines. Mumford, Giedion, and Fuller all emphasize that whereas man adapts to early machines (shoveling coal into the burner of a steam engine), later machines (from the artificial lung to the electric toaster) adapt to man.

Yet these comments only suggest the machine's structure in relation to society. Is there any acceptable, single definition? The most famous one, which serves as the basis for the entry in most modern dictionaries, belongs to Franz Reuleaux (1876): "A machine is a combination of resistant bodies so arranged that by their means the mechanical forces of nature can be compelled to do work accompanied by certain determinant motions." Yet such a definition begs as many questions as it answers. How does a solid-state television set relate to this concept of the machine? This definition limits the machine to "mechanical forces"—it assumes forms of energy available through natural sources and operated by means of an organization of interchangeable parts. Čapek's robots don't fit very comfortably into such a definition—nor do Norbert Wiener's computers, which he frequently refers to as machines.

Two distinctions must be made here. The first is that between mechanical and electronic technologies. McLuhan, Wiener, and Fuller have stressed this distinction: from interchangeable parts to integrated circuits, from the consumption of natural energy sources to new routes for tapping and channeling energies, from the bit-by-bit method of mechanization to the all-at-once method of electronic technology. "Machine" may be a word that has passed into common parlance to describe new as well as old technologies; but strictly speaking, electronic instruments are not machines, and the electronic age is not the machine age.

The second distinction relates to the way in which Mumford, Giedion, and Ellul conceive of machines. The nature and direction of their work has disposed them to define machines (if only implicitly) in terms of their *effects* rather than their internal structures. For Mumford a machine is what defines the new energy level of a society. For Giedion it is the heart of the mechanization of society. For Ellul it is the springboard for technique, which proceeds to spread into the recesses of society. Mumford, Giedion, and Ellul suggest that machines can best be defined in terms of their relationship to society; other, structural, definitions tend to draw our attention away from what these men regard as the central fact of the machine—what it does to man.

We may not quite know who Golem is, but we fear what he can do. The man of clay, resurrected as the man of bolts and gears, may have been welcomed enthusiastically at first. Now there are those who find him an unpleasant guest.

FACES OF THE MACHINE

"Give me a lever long enough," said Archimedes, "and I will move the world." In the eighteenth century Descartes gave the Newtonian equivalent: "Let me have extension and motion, and I will remake the world; the universe is a machine in which everything happens by figures and motion."

The universe as machine served as the great metaphor for the eighteenth-century rationalist philosophers. The heavens moved with the harmony of fine clockwork; planets and suns followed their paths with mechanical precision. Such an image sprang not only from Newton's bold mechanistic physics, but also from the popular intellectual pretension that reason could explain the whole universe as easily as the workings of a machine, however intricate.

The idea has colored the ways in which the machine has been interpreted until very recently. If all of nature is one vast machine, then what is man? The plight of industrial workers in the mid-nineteenth century led to a recognition among literary and conservative groups that the machine was remaking man in its own likeness. This led, in turn, not only to loudly voiced criticisms of the machine and the capitalists it most benefited, but likewise to what Mumford calls "a retreat from the machine." "The successes of mechanism only increased the awareness of values not included in a mechanistic ideology—values derived, not from the machine, but from other provinces of life."

Three of the most significant attacks on the machine before the appearance of Mumford, Giedion, and Ellul were made by Samuel Butler, Henry Adams, and Friedrich Georg Juenger. Each of these criticisms anticipates in some way later analyses to be seen in the coming chapters.

Samuel Butler's *Erewhon* appeared in 1872. *Erewhon* is no utopian tract but the work of a scathing satirist. Butler rips into the Church, the political and economic myths of the time, the fashions and decorum of Victorian England. Yet despite its satiric vein, *Erewhon* recognized a range of themes that only later would become major questions. As Lewis Mumford has stated in the introduction to a recent edition, "In short, Butler's wildest jokes are nearer to present-day truths than many sober Victorian platitudes." This is particularly true of Butler's discussion of the machine.

Three chapters of *Erewhon* are titled "The Book of the Machines." They were based on a letter Butler had written to the Christchurch *Press* in New Zealand, where Butler was living, in 1863. The essay, later retitled "Darwin Among the Machines," suggests that Darwin's theory of evolution applies to machines as well as to living organisms. "We have used the words 'mechanical life,' 'the mechanical kingdom,' 'the mechanical world,' and so forth, and we have done so advisedly, for as the vegetable kingdom was slowly developed from the mineral, and as in like manner the animal supervened upon the vegetable, so now in these last few ages an entirely new kingdom has sprung up, of which we as yet have only seen what will one day be considered the antediluvian prototypes of the race."

Machines, Butler recommends, should be classified into their genera and species; their organs, such as "the little protuberance at the bottom of the bowl of our tobacco pipe," studied for clues to evolutionary history. As with the mighty dinosaurs, large size will capitulate to a smaller, more adaptable form. One day, for example, clocks may all be replaced by watches.

But the final meaning of evolution among machines is that one day the machines will inherit the earth. And man will applaud the creation he has made, the creation that displaces him. "In the course of ages we shall find ourselves the inferior race. Inferior in power, inferior in that moral quality of self-control, we shall look up to them as the acme of all that the best and wisest man can ever dare to aim at. No evil passions, no jealousy, no avarice, no impure desires will disturb the serene might of those glorious creatures."

Butler was aiming his fire at the twin infatuations of the time: popularized Darwinism and the belief that mechanisms were beckoning the way to the promised land. But history has shown that the satire was veined with prophecy. Writing almost a hundred years later, Norbert Wiener, an early designer of information science, described the computer in terms that startlingly parallel some of Butler's supposedly satiric remarks. Wiener writes, "Now that certain analogies of behavior are being observed between the machine and the living organism, the problem as to whether the machine is alive or not is, for our purposes, semantic and we are at liberty to answer it one way or the other as best suits our convenience." Says Butler, "But who can say that a vapor engine has no kind of consciousness? Where does consciousness begin, and where end? Who can draw the line? Who can draw any line?"

Says Wiener, "there is no reason why they [the machines] may not resemble human beings in representing pockets of decreasing entropy* in a framework in which the larger entropy tends to increase"—the possibility of a valid evolution of machines, couched in the language of modern mathematics. Says Butler, "It appears to us that we are ourselves creating our own successors; we are daily adding to the beauty and delicacy of their physical organization; we are daily giving them greater power and supplying by all sorts of ingenious contrivances that self-regulating, self-acting power which will be to them what intellect has been to the human race."

Butler did not play on fear of the machines, but on his contemporaries' faith in them. Henry Adams takes a distinctly

* Entropy is the tendency of energy to disperse, and of a system to run down.

different approach: the machine's forces become the model for a theory of history.

Adams was one of the great schematic historians, attempting like Auguste Comte and Carl Becker to find a pattern or a set of rules that underlies the process of history. As Roderick Seidenberg has commented, "certainly among historians no one has been as insistent as Henry Adams in attempting to establish a relationship between the historic process and the Phase Rule of Willard Gibbs in an effort to achieve that science of history which he believed to be firmly implied in the universal formulae of thermodynamics." In the phase rule, Gibbs developed a method whereby, if several factors of a system were known, the probable state of the other factors could be determined. The relationship between the universal law of entropy and the tendency of any system to seek new available energies before running down is a theme that Adams drew from Gibbs and applied to the study of history. The significance of the machine and machine systems becomes immediately obvious. As Wiener comments, machines are basically systems for fighting entropy; and as systems become more complex and integrated (as with computers), the anti-entropic tendency, previously limited to man, becomes a pronounced feature of the machine world. Adams's theory of history emphasizes its great institutions (the Church, the feudal system, Roman law) as ever declining, according to the principle of entropy. Yet in this process of decline every system searches for new possibilities of resolution. As Adams comments in his famous essay, "A Dynamic Theory of History," "A dynamic law requires that two masses—nature and man—must go on, reacting upon each other, without stop, as the sun and a comet react on each other, and that any appearance of stoppage is illusive."

Friedrich Georg Juenger's *The Failure of Technology* is highly representative of a strong twentieth-century tradition of attacks upon the machine—ranging from sociologists like Ortega y Gasset and Robert Jungk to writers like D. H. Lawrence. Juenger's treatment is important for its identification of technology with death (for both polemic and metaphysical reasons) and its seminal relationship to a later work of similar thrust, though of far greater scope: Jacques Ellul's *The Technological Society.*

Juenger opposes the organic and the mechanical as two principles that, no matter how complex their interaction, cannot successfully combine into a single whole. Instead, the mechanical—for Juenger the death principle—subtly and gradually invades and corrodes the organic. "Clock time is lifeless time, *tempus mortuum,* in which the second follows second in monotonous repetition. . . . To the reflective mind, the clock summons up the thought of death. The figure of the dying Charles V, pacing among the clocks in his collection and attempting to regulate their movements, emits the frost of death."

Juenger attacks technology for its destruction of human will and feeling, for the myths it has introduced and fostered, for the specialization and functionalism it brings about—in short, he resounds the whole familiar panoply of fears about technology. His method is heavy-handed, his tone vitriolic. Consider some sample chapter titles: "The Pillage of the Earth"; "The Invasion of Life by Dead Time"; "The Perversion of Freedom"; "Self-deception by Photography"; "The Mechanical Sterility of Modern Sports."

Yet Juenger was one of the first to raise (if not to pursue) questions about the range of technological influence. Technology restructures not only the way we think, but the basic emotional responses we are capable of having toward experience. Juenger was among the first to apply Alfred Adler's "will to power" to the growth of modern technology. Likewise he saw the state persisting as an illusion, whereas technology had actually usurped its powers and potentialities—a theme common not only to Ellul, but to Innis, McLuhan, and Fuller as well.

Finally, one must ask: is the failure of technology simply the failure of technology—or of man? The questions and assumptions inherent in most of the thought about machines, from Čapek to Juenger, from Mumford to Ellul, begins with the premise of a basic opposition between organic and mechanistic forms. Is this opposition valid? What are its implications? What are its alternatives? Does the denial of the machine lead, inevitably, to a denial of the future in a technological society?

BOOTPRINT OF THE MACHINE

"If you want a picture of the future," states O'Brien in George Orwell's *1984*, "imagine a boot stamping on the human face—forever." In varying degrees, Mumford, Giedion, and Ellul have turned to the past to summon a similar image: what the machine has wrought upon humanity.

What is it about the machine, in its pre-electronic forms, that has drawn such negative and severe reaction? Its metallic strangeness? Its restructuring of time and space? Its social and economic consequences? Its tendency to standardize a culture? Its subtle subversion of the values of work, individualism, craftsmanship? Its creation of a mass society? Its trend toward rationalism? Its organization of parts?

There are distinct and separate arguments for each of these —for example, Roderick Seidenberg's *Post-Historic Man* (organization), Ortega y Gasset's *The Revolt of the Masses* (mass society), Herbert Marcuse's *One Dimensional Man* (standardization and homogeneity). As attractive as the single theory is, the history of the machine and its reverberations in society (described best by Mumford in *Technics and Civili-*

zation) reveals that both cause and effect tend to be diverse and largely unpredictable. Indeed, "the machine" is only a metaphorical label for a far more complex and diversified phenomenon than the word suggests.

What is this phenomenon? Mumford uses the term "technics," Giedion "mechanization," Ellul "technique." These terms and the ways they are used to measure the technological impact upon a society represent three distinct but overlapping patterns. Mumford defines "technics" as energy tools, or machines—always existing within cultural and technological contexts. The term is broad, and more functional than analytical. For Giedion, "mechanization" is the process whereby the characteristics of a machine (or a machine-inspired method) become translated into social and cultural experience. For example, in following the mechanization of bread, Giedion shows the historical steps that led from the firm, nutritious bread of pre-industrial times to today's supermarket fluff. Where Mumford focuses on the larger patterns of technical innovations, Giedion pokes into the corners and hideaways of history to show exactly how everyday phenomena, from bread-making to furniture, becomes mechanized.

If Mumford's technics and Giedion's mechanization are descriptive terms, Jacques Ellul's technique is metaphysical. Ellul accepts Harold Lasswell's definition of technique as "the ensemble of practices by which one uses available resources in order to achieve certain valued ends," but this can barely hint at the final meanings Ellul requires of the term. For Ellul, technique is the life-force of a technological society; it represents the principle of the machine (quantitative, standardized, organizational, totally rational and predictable) becoming the principle of society—the final acquiescence of man to the machine.

These definitions suggest basic similarities and differences in these three approaches to the machine. Among the most important similarities are the assumption of a basic opposition between organic life and the machine, the triumph of quantity over quality in the impact of the machine upon a culture, and the assumption that technologies shape a society far more than is generally recognized by the people in that society or by later historians.

The idea of a basic conflict between man and the machine, rather than a principle of continuity, has already been treated and will reappear throughout this book as a central theme. It is so basic to Mumford, Giedion, and Ellul that none of them even questions or analyzes it.

Quantity and quality are old and familiar measuring devices, dating from Aristotle and earlier. The most evident single thread that the three thinkers follow between the machine and society is its usurpation of qualitative judgment by quantitative judgment. The simplest example is the clock. One of Mumford's best chapters is devoted to the impact of the clock upon culture, and Giedion pursues the development of time-motion efficiency studies with a fine flair. Ellul considers our dependence on the mechanical rhythms of the clock one of the major symptoms of the extent of technology's encroachment on twentieth-century civilization.

All three men assume that the machine transforms a culture to a greater extent than the people in that culture generally realize. Mumford has shown some fascinating relationships between such developments as the rise of industrial capitalism and the emergence of new sports. Giedion's precise history shows how, for example, new concepts of the bath have emerged partly from technical innovations in plumbing. Ellul begins his book by stating that he is "diagnosing a disease" while the culture remains oblivious to the existence of it.

Concomitant with these similarities are a range of differences, three of which remain distinctive. The problem of new and old technologies was mentioned in the previous chapter;

in many ways it serves as a contemporary restatement for the ancient problem of persistence and change. The problem takes on particularly large dimensions in the technological sphere. Here the very value of the thought of these men—who have concentrated on mechanical, rather than electronic, machines—is at stake. To phrase the question simply: is the laser an updated bow and arrow, or a radically new kind of phenomenon?

Mumford considers technics as a principle of modification within a larger persisting framework, namely culture. His three "phases" of technical growth (eotechnic, paleotechnic, and neotechnic) serve less to emphasize the importance of change than to underscore the primacy of persistence. Giedion's work, as far as it goes, suggests that change occurs on all levels but the organic and the immediate needs felt by the organic. Less immediate needs can be shaped and changed, however, just as the environment that shapes them is transformed by the process of mechanization.

Ellul posits a principle of drastic change in the introduction of technique—which he locates within the seventeenth century. But the introduction of technics, he suggests, guarantees a fresh principle of continuity—perhaps the only principle of continuity available to our age.

Another basis for critical difference lies in the concept of history that each of these men introduces. Mumford and Giedion are explicitly writing histories; Ellul uses a great deal of historical data, but does not consider himself a historian (indeed, he apologizes more than once for his inadequacy at the task). For Mumford, history serves to reveal the larger patterns that the interaction between technics and culture have created. The historian is a geographer, mapping the larger terrains of time; the historian of technics is simply following a heretofore ignored set of geological landmarks. Giedion has subtitled *Mechanization Takes Command* "A Contribution to

Anonymous History." With some modifications, his history might be considered Mumford's history writ small; to continue a worn metaphor, the geographer mapping his land on foot. Ellul writes thesis history. The phenomena he discusses overlap with Mumford's, but take on a radical significance, since for Ellul they illuminate the development of technique.

Finally, the three men differ on precisely what constitutes man's relationship to the machine. In a general sense, they agree that by creating a new environment, technology introduces into society new constructs of thought and action, new rhythms and images, new needs and expectations. But Mumford interprets the exact nature of the action of technology in terms of energy levels; Giedion primarily in terms of space and time; Ellul as an almost mystical process of metanoia—total transformation of society via technique.

In *The Age of Discontinuity,* Peter Drucker has remarked that even in the second half of the twentieth century, the dominant volume in business still deals with technologies that follow patterns set in the nineteenth. The mechanical technologies so familiar to twentieth-century man (movies or the electric stove) are basically nineteenth-century forms. Our culture has yet to be completely rescaled by electronic environments, though this appears increasingly imminent. In a period of transition or "technological overlap," it is as important to understand the impact of the coming environments as to know what we are leaving behind.

Technics and Civilization, Mechanization Takes Command, and *The Technological Society* were all written in the twentieth century. But it is perhaps their central inherent weakness that each deals essentially with pre-twentieth century phenomena, and in a nineteenth-century framework of thought. Giedion acknowledges this; he ventures into the twentieth century only to follow earlier patterns through. Mumford's discussion of the neotechnic or contemporary era is clearly the weakest section of his book—precisely because he attempts to use the methods and constructs of older technics on the new age. Ellul consciously grapples with the twentieth century, but his focus is undermined by his method, the highly organized, comprehensive treatise of nineteenth-century science.

These men have seen the Golem, but they cannot tell us whether he abides in an age where his clay, after turning to metal, has been replaced by plastic. Despite all they have said of the machine—and they have said some of the most perceptive things yet about it—the question remains: is their interpretation basically prophetic or precluded by the world they never quite saw?

THREE

The View from the Citadel

LEWIS MUMFORD

> Like a drunken locomotive engineer on a streamlined train, plunging through the darkness at a hundred miles an hour, we have been going past the danger signals without realizing that our speed, which springs from our mechanical facility, only increases our danger and will make more fatal the crash.
>
> Lewis Mumford, *Art and Technics*

One of the ironies surrounding the study of the machine and its historical development is that its greatest commentators, from Siegfried Giedion to Norbert Wiener, have not been the machine's apologists, but its harshest critics. Of no one is this so true as of Lewis Mumford.

Mumford's humanism is so pervasive as to be instinctive. Throughout his major work, *Technics and Civilization* (1934), he interprets historical developments according to their humanizing or dehumanizing effects, and on balance emerges with an optimistic outlook. Later works, such as *Art and Technics, The Transformations of Man,* and particularly *The Myth of the Machine,* reflect a different prospect—darker, less promising for man, weighted in favor of the machine.

It would be unfair to call Mumford a historian of technics, though no one, not even Giedion, is more deserving of the phrase. Mumford's great achievement in his works on technics, as in his many works on architecture, is to set the growth of one phenomenon within the larger context of cultural evolution. Ellul's vision of techniques as an autonomous force careening through history, as well as McLuhan's more subversive interpretation of history, have no ground in Mumford. The machine is a product and a problem of our culture and its history; Mumford is never as trenchant as in giving perspective to either aspect.

Indeed, if a single word could characterize the entire Mumford opus, it would be perspective. Mumford struggles to enable his reader to envision mighty historical processes in their entirety. It is a great overarching view, as from a citadel. Invariably he stresses relationships over discrepancies, continuities over discontinuities, forms of persistence over cycles of change. In *Technics and Civilization,* for example, he is careful to characterize the three great periods of technics as *phases* rather than ages. More important than their individual distinctiveness is their relation to the whole. And it is the whole, the *gestalt* of cultural history, that Mumford wants to convey.

The complete body of Mumford's works is large and varied. His architectural studies, his monumental works on the city, and his unique contributions to cultural history fall mostly outside our present scope; any of them cited here will be only for brief references and clarifications. This study will focus on Mumford's specific contribution to an understanding of the technological environment as set forth in *Technics and Civilization* (1934), *Art and Technics* (1952), and *The Myth of the Machine* (1966). Briefly, a note follows about each of these books.

Technics and Civilization, one of Mumford's earliest works, remains his major contribution to an understanding of the machine in history. Before Giedion had coined the phrase "anonymous history," Mumford had explored its unique terrain. (Not that Mumford was the earliest; Henry Adams, J. Beckmann, and Patrick Geddes had all done important work in the cultural effects of technical innovations. None achieved the scale or synthesis, however, of Mumford's study.) By following the three phases of technical developments in Western culture, the eotechnic, the paleotechnic, and the neotechnic, Mumford presents a penetrating view of the complex interactions between technics and cultural history; indeed, nowhere is any interpretation, including Giedion's, so notable for exploring inner dynamics between the machine and the society that created and is modified by the machine. Mumford wrote *Technics and Civilization* in an era that was yet optimistic about the machine and its potential for a new integration of man and his environment; thirty years later, in *The Myth of the Machine,* his earlier confidence would be tempered by reevaluation of what he calls "megatechnics."

In the 1970s, Mumford's historically grounded humanism may seem quaint, even romantic, studded with unabashed manifestos. *Technics and Civilization* ends with a plea for a humanistic socialism to curb the dangers of technics in the hands of capitalists; *The Myth of the Machine,* despite its erudition, is sounded on a shrill note and its scholarship edges on an almost desperate apologetic. *Art and Technics,* originally delivered as a series of lectures at Columbia University in 1951, is essentially Mumford's manifesto for an integration of the machine into the arts. Man must subsume the machine, Mumford argues, not the reverse, which can lead only to the climax anticipated in his analogy of the streamlined locomotive and the drunken engineer.

Mumford's works after World War II combine his resourceful scholarship with a contentious thrust against the dangers and myths of our time. Nowhere is this combination as evident as in *The Myth of the Machine,* primarily an argument against the definition of man as a tool-making animal, and only secondarily a history. Mumford claims that man's image of himself as a modifier of his environment lies at the core of his technological obsession, and in *The Myth of the Machine,* he argues that culture—the complex of language, ritual, art, music, myth, and religion—preceded technics, indeed gave birth to it. The most dominant of Mumfordian themes, the ultimate primacy of the cultural context, has at last found its own manifesto.

Virtually all Mumford's significant writings on the machine (as distinct from his writings on architecture) are historical in character; yet Mumford could not rightly be called a historian of technics. The focus of his work is cultural, often following philosophical and literary contexts. He hews to the broadly based tradition of Adams, Geddes, Spengler, and Frey, rather than the more concentrated study of technics that can be seen in Feldhaus, Giedion, or studies such as Lynn White's *Medieval Technology and Social Change.*

More than anyone else, Mumford is indebted to Patrick Geddes, an earlier historian of technics, one of the earliest sociologists to take on the complex problems of human ecology. Paraphrasing Geddes, he states a premise basic to his own outlook: "Every form of life . . . is marked not merely by adjustment to the environment, but by insurgence against the environment; it is both creature and creator, both the victim of faith and the master of destiny; it lives no less by domination than by acceptance." Geddes's focus on context, his original distinction between paleotechnic and neotechnic culture, his fascination with the dynamic interaction between the organic and its inorganic environment, as well as his thesis that biological structures provide the minuscule framework for sociological phenomena gave Mumford important building blocks for *Technics and Civilization.*

Mumford's methodology in approaching technics follows three principles: the qualitative impact of new materials and energy sources; dynamic interaction; and the advantage of focus over thesis. Each of these principles implicitly gives man, and not technics, the initiative in determining cultural change.

For Mumford, the key to a phase of technology is the material that shapes it and the source of energy that vitalizes it. Thus in the paleotechnic age, seen most graphically in the nineteenth century, iron and coal were the dominant forces. The dark, subterranean world of the miners' lives, the use of iron sinks and iron walls, the negation of color for the black-gray monotony of buildings, rooms, and dress, were as significant for the cultural environment as were the implications of strip mining for the natural environment. In approaching technics, Mumford invariably focuses on qualitative rather than quantitative changes, suggesting that the final repercussions of a new machine are inaccessible to the statistician or the scientist but visible to the culturally sensitized.

Mumford's second principle affirms that culture and technics interact dynamically, that causes are rarely simple and singular, but exist within a shifting framework of ideas, inventions, economies, and needs. Mumford is extraordinarily adept at depicting the process of interaction, and usually avoids the tendency, common among historians dealing with technics, to oppose technics to their cultural context.

The third principle is focus. This is more applicable in *Technics and Civilization* than *The Myth of the Machine,* where thesis overshadows focus. Rather than argue a particular thesis of technics in his early work, Mumford chose to focus on certain aspects of the interaction between technics and culture, which emerge thematically throughout the work. For example, he borrows the phrase "cultural pseudomorph" from Spengler: an analogy to the geological phenomenon of a rock that retains its shape after certain elements have been leached out of it and are replaced by new materials. The automobile replaced the horse and carriage in external structure only; the mechanical nature of the car and its tendency to spawn more of its kind far faster than the horse and carriage gave it an entirely different significance, but one that was hardly recognized by city politicians and urban designers in the crucial early years. Cultural pseudomorphs are a common and perhaps a necessarily recurrent motif in the history of technics and society.

Methodology, finally, is only a tool for Mumford; his vision and his perspective are established elsewhere. There can be no question here whether his total treatment of technics preceded or followed upon the conclusions. It is significant that Mumford's first book was a critique of utopianism. While lauding the conception of utopia as an organic whole (a value he refers back to Geddes), he describes in his preface his growing fear of the danger in any utopia, stating implicitly the values that dominate his historical works on technics and society:

> But once beyond Plato, I was aware of the dictatorial tendencies of most classic utopias. They sought to impose a monolithic discipline upon all the varied activities and interplaying interests of human society, by creating an order too inflexible, and a system of government too centralized and absolute, to permit any change that would disturb the pattern or meet the new exigencies of life. In other words, each utopia was a closed society for the prevention of human growth; and the more the institutions of utopia succeeded in stamping the minds of its members, the less possibility existed of furthering creative and purposeful change. *(The Story of Utopias)*

THE AGES OF MAN-MACHINE

History, to Lewis Mumford, is less important for where it is going than for where it has been. This is another way of saying that Mumford eschews evolutionary or vitalistic theories of history and tends to view it rather as a great human excursion, filled with blind alleys and false routes. Technics itself, in its present gargantuan development, may indeed be one of its greatest, and possibly most misleading, routes.

The forces that move history are not as much events or men as the crystallization of cultural relationships. Although he seldom uses the term, Mumford's concept of "syncretism" dominates his work, particularly *Technics and Civilization.* Syncretism is the fusion of two beliefs or practices into a third, and sometimes original, form. A similar idea, 'sometimes called "synergy" (Fuller) or "interface" (McLuhan) runs through the thinking of most of the other men described in this book. The growth of nationalistic armies in the sixteenth century influenced and was in turn influenced by new, gunpowder-based weapons, particularly the cannon. That syncretic relationship tended not only to give the armies more destructive power than ever before, but sparked a fresh lust for power reaching far beyond the armies, into the realms of finance and national leadership.

Mumford's history of technics centers on three phases: the eotechnic phase (roughly A.D. 1000 to 1750), the paleotechnic phase (after 1750), and the neotechnic phase (just emerging in the twentieth century). Each phase is largely characterized by the major source of materials and energy that dominated it. The eotechnic phase was powered by wind and water, continuous resources whose use tends to conserve rather than corrupt the natural environment. Coal, however, which energized the paleotechnic phase, was a resource that diminished with use; this phase marked the apex of man's ruthless power in enforcing economic servility and raping the countryside through strip mining and pollution.

The lines that Mumford draws between a phase's materials and its dominant cultural effects are clean and simple, indicating a historical method that follows the shortest route between two phenomena.

Mumford's three phases are only incidentally historical, in that they do not mark conventional historical periods but rather the dominating cultural influence of certain ages. In *The Culture of Cities* he later made a distinction between dominant and recessive cultural traits; the dominant traits give a cultural period its immediate appearance and flavor; the recessive traits give it the undercurrent of forces that continue older institutions and practices. Even as the dominant force of one phase wears down, its hallmarks become present in a recessive way in the next phase. Well into the paleotechnic phase the influence of eotechnic methods remained strong. And even today, after the dawn of the neotechnic phase, air pollution, oil and coal mining, the uses of iron, the capitalist economy—all features of the paleotechnic phase—remain influential. Phases do not conclude, but overlap.

Running through the three phases, and partially explicating them, is a major Mumfordian motif: the historical process of the man-machine ratio. Throughout the eotechnic and paleotechnic phases man gradually became adapted to the machine. The clock transformed man's rhythms of eating, sleeping, and working from natural to mechanized ones. Inventions such as the steam engine forced men into the bowels of the earth to supply the needed coal. The early periods of technics gave precedence to the machine, not man, in determining its shape and man's participation in its production and activity.

The neotechnic phase has reversed this tendency; machines are increasingly being adapted to man. The automobile, the airplane, the computer, radio, television: all mark a fresh departure for technics. Here the design of the machine, and more important, its cultural repercussions, tend to make the machine adapt to man rather than the reverse.

The tendency of the machine to adapt to man is only beginning; it will reach its climax, no doubt, in "thinking" computers and in cyborgs, those electronic suits of armor that one day men may wear, extending all their muscles and senses, permitting mechanical "supermen" to walk virtually naked on foreign planets.

The process of the machine's adjusting itself to man is not as one-sided as it may seem. In *Art and Technics* Mumford notes that man is still being adapted, though in subtler ways, to the machine, suggesting that the older process is continuing, though "recessively."

Each of Mumford's three phases depends upon a mechanism that utilizes energy in a new way and introduces a new machine that modifies its cultural context. These mechanisms vary, of course, with the cultures and the nature of the technical innovation. Those triggered by a new energy source tend to operate subliminally, so that we notice only their effects and causes, but not the direct causal route.

The clock, for example, is the keystone of the paleotechnic phase, not simply because it shaped further technics, but more critically, because it organized man's experience of time. In earlier periods, man's work and leisure were related to the seasons and to the sunrise and sunset. Precise measurement of hours, minutes, and seconds had no place in his experience of time. When the clock came into use, it created the cultural environment necessary for the development and introduction of the newer technics, which were based on regulated speed, such as the timing by which engines are fueled. The clock did far more than standardize and neutralize time; it was, as Mumford states, "a new kind of power-machine, in which the source of power and the transmission were of such a nature as to insure the even flow of energy throughout the works and to make possible regular production and a standardized product." As the abstract framework of the clock's time became the basis for human activities, time became a commodity and people began to think of it as something to be saved or filled. It was spatialized; it could be divided, expanded, enclosed.

While it is true that individual machines can operate outside the framework of organized time, the total technological complex would collapse without the clock at its foundation. Try to imagine New York City for one day without clocks. It would be jeopardized far more than by the loss of electricity.

With the clock, as with other power machines, energy imparts itself to society through the distinct character of the power exerted by the machine. The product of the clock is an abstract, and finally a spatialized, breakdown of time. The products of other power machines vary from the hunger of power stoked by early cannons to the pacesetting significance of the steam engine.

Sometimes the machine permeates culture by becoming a surrogate for human experience. This can be seen vividly with movies and television, where the fantasy needs of a culture are satisfied by mechanical means; but it is true as well of early weapons, which transformed the scale of human conflict by interposing between men new and more destructive warfare, requiring new kinds of armor and defense. Machines at once extend and protect man, encasing his nakedness with their harder, less supple forms; yet rather than extending and protecting his experiences, they subtly tend to supplant them, making them more mechanized, less direct and real, more dependent upon technical forms than upon man's initiative. Mumford thus assumes that one of the graver impacts of technics has been to discourage creativity and personal expression; rather than sing or hum, people listen to the radio, a vital loss, Mumford claims, because man is now permitting the machine to dictate his experiences, ones that are necessarily of a far inferior quality and impede, rather than help, human growth.

In the early chapters of *Technics and Civilization,* Mumford focuses on the cultural preparation for technics and the agents of technics: the religious and magical forces that obstructed yet anticipated later technics; the economic conditions; the importance of warfare in sparking invention and later spreading new discoveries; the military as a model and cultural conditioner of the proper environment for the development and use of technics. The growth of technics snowballed in Western culture after the sixteenth century. The reasons for this acceleration, Mumford suggests, are to be found less in the precise nature of the technics themselves than in the cultural readiness for a series of overlapping technical revolutions. China had long before invented and propagated paper, as well as block printing and movable type. But nowhere in its prehistory, whether in China, Japan, Korea, India, Turkey, Persia, Egypt, Arabia, or Russia, did the printing press have an influence on its culture equivalent to its impact on the eotechnic phase of European culture.

The growth of technics constitutes a historical development unparalleled at any time in man's previous existence. Mumford distinguishes between tools, which lend themselves to manipulation, and machines, which function automatically. The cultural consequences of the two forms symbolize the distinction between the age of technics and the previous age of tools. "In general, the machine emphasizes specialization of function, whereas the tool indicates flexibility." The differences in the degree of specialization and the degree of impersonality fostered by the machine would underscore the unique departure of the age of technics from any period of the past.

The Eotechnic Phase (1000–1750)

"The dawn age of modern technics," as Mumford calls it, is that period emerging from the dissolution of medieval Christianity and gradually reshaping the focus and expectations of

Renaissance Europe. The eotechnic period, for its simplicity of origin—wood, water and wind power, glass—unleashed energies in Western culture that have still not quieted; it tore man's gaze from the heavens and refocused it upon the earth; it challenged man with his own image in the mirror, spinning his consciousness from its earlier, religious orbits into the new subjective galaxy that was the central discovery of the Renaissance. The new machines and sources of energy were primitive and irregular. The mechanization of culture was only a glimmer of what it would be in later centuries. However, the eotechnic period slowly awoke a people to the possibilities of their environment; it gave them the first materials and energy sources to explore the physical world that they had so long ignored. Above all, it triggered a new scale of thinking and responding, a new attitude toward life, which was to be the final and most important product of the age.

The underlying force behind the eotechnic period was not invention, but assimilation, what Mumford calls "technical syncretism." Most of the innovations of that period were borrowed, not original; the water mill, the windmill, the horseshoe, and the harness all had predecessors. While some degree of invention gave them their own European character and adaptability, these innovations were more significant for their long-range impact on European culture than for their stimulus to similar, if more complex, technical development.

Water and wind provided the power for threshing, grinding, hammering, pulping rags for paper, beating hides for tanning; wood provided the material that enabled men to build the windmill or the water mill. Wood is the ideal material for experimentation and the early development of technics. Its tensile strength, its ready availability, its structural adaptability, its easiness to transport and to shape with primitive tools; all these factors made it not only the universal material of the eotechnic period, but also the necessary precursor of more specialized materials such as iron, the alloys, and eventually the lighter metals and plastics. The extensive shaping and tooling of wood was itself a minor revolution of this period, resulting in new architecture, experimentation with technics that would later be translated into metals, and above all, a fresh thrust in shipbuilding and water transport.

If wood shaped the technics of the period, glass shaped its mental universe. Glass making, a discovery dating back to the Egyptians, became popular along with the growing use of wood in constructing buildings. It transformed buildings and people's experience of them by changing interior light quality and introducing the frame. "Glass helped put the word in a frame," Mumford writes. "It made it possible to see certain elements of reality more clearly, and it focused attention on a sharply defined field—namely, that which was bounded by the frame."

Glass can serve two functions: to convey light and vision, and to reflect images. Mumford sees the second function, prompted by the mirror, as the final significance of glass in the eotechnic phase. The mirror enabled people to see, virtually for the first time, an image of themselves that corresponded accurately with what others saw. It made men conscious of themselves as never before; introspection became a life style, one that, indeed, was to dominate the Renaissance and later periods.

Through glass, eotechnic man beheld a new world that beckoned for change and modification. The inventions of several centuries drew men closer to this new world, but no invention did this as much as the experimental method in science. The old order rested upon faith that the stars and the earth were fixed parts in a system devised by God to reveal His glory. The experimental method substituted a drastically different concept of order that explained nature, rather than fostering its mysterious character, and that prepared the way for standardization and mechanization.

The advantages of the eotechnic phase were on an equal par with its weaknesses. Water is an irregular source of power, and wind is even more so. Textile mills, for example, might employ their workers two days one week, five the next. Moreover, the growing concentration of the new sources of energy created a fresh system of work depending less on the internal discipline of the workshop and more on the external discipline imposed by the employer. Marx has shown how even in the beginnings of the eotechnic period the early glimmer of capitalism, combined with its unique dangers, was apparent. Yet in the eotechnic period machines, products, and buildings were built to last; craftsmanship remained the style of production. Many of the new technics, such as the telescope and eyeglasses, served to extend and refine man's senses, sharpening his response to the external world. Many of the contributions of the eotechnic period remain with us in gardens, the best of city designs, the wood crafts in furniture design. The eotechnic period, in its best and its worst, was only a beginning, the presage of events yet to come. As Mumford concludes, "The rift between mechanization and humanization, between power bent on its own aggrandizement and power directed toward wider human fulfillment had already appeared, but its consequences had yet to become fully visible."

The Paleotechnic Phase (1750 to 1900)

The Industrial Revolution, which dominated Europe, England, and America in the nineteenth century, is generally considered the turning point of the technical revolution. Mumford places the shift in the middle of the eighteenth century, when the eotechnic period had run its course and new materials and new sources of power were introduced into industry and life.

The term "paleotechnic" is drawn from Geddes, notably his *Cities in Evolution.* There he likened the earlier and later phases of the industrial revolution to the corresponding phases of the stone age, the first (paleo) crude, the second (neo) refined. Mumford extends the paleotechnic period well into the twentieth century; in his terms only with the gradual introduction of electronic and highly sophisticated technologies did the neotechnic age emerge.

The paleotechnic phase is largely one in which the inventions of the eotechnic phase are consolidated and systematized. More important, however, is the degree to which the paleotechnic phase was able to create new institutions built around the technics, from capitalism to the shape of modern armies. The paleotechnic phase gave technics its first grand taste of control of a culture on all its levels. A fresh lust for power characterized the paleotechnic period, and that power reached into every recess of human life.

Mumford describes the paleotechnic era as an experiment in the "quantification of life." Iron and coal needed a more concentrated base than earlier materials and energy sources. Both had to be mined from the earth, and mining required capital investment and workers. Steam engines needed coal, the exploitation of which led to the exploitation of man. The age was, by its own blind technical vitality, "upthrust into barbarism."

Steam proved to be a mixed blessing. It gave industry a new impetus, provided the first technical basis for speedy transportation, and widened the ambits of industrial energies. But to operate a steam-powered factory required considerably more capital than earlier factories run on the free energy of wind or water. Furnaces had to be stoked twenty-four hours a day in order not to waste heat. Big engines created big factories requiring large investment. Power and wealth thus became concentrated by the economic demands of coal and steam.

Corresponding social concentrations began, of industrial and mining towns, of geographical areas drawn together by the railroads.

Iron and coal gave a grim overcast to the era. The uses of iron were extended to almost preposterous functions: for walls, building faces, buttons, and doors. And the deep cloudy black of the coal gradually became the universal color, seen in boots, stovepipe hats, carriages, cooking pots, pans, stoves, books, clothing. The countryside and the sky darkened as factories spewed out the black gritty smoke day and night. But the great sin of the period was social. Mumford sketches ugly moments: the practice of supplementing flour with plaster and milk with embalming fluid; the almost systematic starvation of the senses through a corruption of the urban environment, smog, and the bad conditions of mine and factory; the degradation of women and children as seen in the incident of naked women miners creating a moral outrage among the upper classes, not for working fourteen hours a day hauling coal, but for doing it without clothes.

As power became concentrated, quantitative standards came to control most outlooks. Labor became a resource, with man-hours as precisely figured as horsepower. The tempo of life was speeded up to keep pace with the new machines, and time became increasingly standardized, guiding every minute of life. Mechanical time became second nature. Indeed, for people working long hours in the factories at a mechanical tempo, it supplanted the normal rhythms of their lives, throwing askew the organic and sexual rhythms.

Mumford finds it ironic that the educated classes of the paleotechnic era "regarded their own period—which was in fact a low one measured by almost any standard except scientific thought and raw energy—as the natural peak of humanity's ascent to date." Darwin's theory of evolution became the apologia for grave social injustice.

Mumford states that the paleotechnic period achieved two things historically: it explored the blind alleys of a quantitative conception of life, and it led to the reaction, equal and vehement, of the neotechnic phase, which would substitute order for its disorder, fundamental to the paleotechnic phase.

The Neotechnic Phase (1900 on)

The neotechnic phase poses special problems. Mumford sees it less as a historically completed phase than as an imminent development in man's technological history. We stand at the verge of this new age, he suggests. And though we can only glimpse slight facets of it, its overall shape is less dismaying than the paleotechnic phase; indeed, Mumford in 1933 felt a relative buoyancy about the neotechnic phase. Here, possibly more than anywhere else in his work, he repudiates the notion that it is in the nature of things for the machine to cripple and endanger man.

The elemental difference between the neotechnic phase and those periods that preceded it are the movement from life patterned on the machine to the machine patterned on life. Instead of factories that estrange and cripple human life, products emerge from automated production units, adapted by the machine to fit any range of sizes or specialized function, from shoes to furniture. (Non-standardized production is usually easier within an automated setting than in a human assembly line.)

In the neotechnic phase science is applied to all of life, and its influence, a new kind of order, becomes pervasive and indeed inevitable. Invention becomes systematic and organized; corporations rather than individuals become the advance guard of scientific progress.

Mumford acknowledges that the new form of energy is electricity, but his understanding of it is limited by its comparative newness at the time he wrote. The distinction, for example, between mechanical and electronic technologies had not yet come into play. Such a distinction is a keystone, decades later, of McLuhan's work, and a dominant theme in Wiener. Mumford views electricity strictly within the ambits and advantages of its power, not within the new networks and speed with which it is able to operate. He tries to fit the criteria of previous epochs to the twentieth century, though they sometimes prove of questionable value in the light of more recent developments.

The new substances of the neotechnic phase are the light metals, chiefly aluminum, and synthetics such as plastics. Their use moves society further and further from the natural materials such as wood and stone. If the paleotechnic phase altered man's environment significantly, the neotechnic phase has virtually reconstituted it.

The great advantage of the neotechnic phase, for Mumford, lies in the shift from quantitative to qualitative standards through automation, which liberates man from inhumane work, and through conservation of environment, population planning, and new discoveries in medicine. Yet the neotechnic phase is likewise burdened by unique difficulties. The most important of these is the prevalence of cultural pseudomorphs, those wineskins of the past that have come to contain our new wine. The automobile is an example. It could have liberated the cities, but since no one seemed to notice what was happening, it only served to congest them further, and cities were redesigned to accommodate not man but the car. The problem of the cultural pseudomorph is even more critical in the economic sphere. "We have merely used our new machines and energies to further processes which were begun under the auspices of capitalist and military enterprise; we have not yet utilized them to conquer these forms of enterprise and subdue them to more vital and humane purposes." In 1933, Mumford seemed confident enough that the future would unshackle the hold of the old on the new.

ENERGY AND SOCIETY

In Mumford's scheme, technics influence culture nowhere so directly or thoroughly as in the new level and forms of energy that they introduce. The clock, therefore, which Mumford perceptively designates a "power-machine," was the first in a series of energy transformations that effected cultural changes of growing magnitude.

Energy operates on several levels within Mumford's construction of the past: as the connecting rod between work and life, as one of the principal currents in the world's shifting economy, as a clue to the qualitative directions of an era, as a mask for the shortcomings of the period it has created, and not least, as the basis for what Mumford terms an "organic ideology." Each of these functions helps clarify Mumford's broad definition of energy, one that is surprisingly close to that of his ideological opponent, Buckminster Fuller.

The most obvious way in which energy changes society is through work and workers. In an eotechnic economy, the energy sources depended on wind and water: irregular, and creating an irregular, or at least only partially mechanized, rhythm on the part of workers. The steam engine not only speeded up the work of factories and transportation forms; it forced the workers to speed up their activities, made the machine the controlling source of timing, and finally sundered men from their earlier, organic rhythms. Giedion has analyzed the process in more detail in *Mechanization Takes Command,* but Mumford recognizes it and gives it attention within each of the phases of technics.

The best of Mumford's work provides categories for a human ecology that includes both technics and culture and is capable of responding to new developments in either realm. Each of the phases that Mumford describes contains its own economy, which derives largely from the distinctive form of energy available to it. In effect, Mumford articulates a ratio between new energy and the proper ideological context in which that energy can best be harnessed. "The private monopoly of coal beds and oil wells," he writes, "is an intolerable anachronism—as intolerable as would be the monopoly of sun, air, running water." His final chapter in *Technics and Civilization,* entitled "Orientation," is largely an argument for a socialist ideology capable of coping positively with the new technics.

One of the ironies of technics is that it leads to a complex of technologies required to overcome the limitations created by earlier technologies. For instance, eggs have to be refrigerated at some expense in order to surmount the problem of time and distance created by the removal of the worker from the countryside. Thorstein Veblen wondered, in *The Instinct of Workmanship*, whether advances such as the typewriter, automobile, and telephone "have not wasted more effort and substance than they have saved." Neither Mumford nor Veblen approached the problem outside of the energy economy that it represents; later McLuhan would suggest the significance underlying these "wasted energies."

Mumford, like his mentor, Patrick Geddes, is fascinated by the interrelations and the dynamics between the organic and the nonorganic. The history of technics since medieval times has followed a single thrust, Mumford claims, toward the adaptation of the organic to the inorganic, of life to the machine. Today, under the impetus of a new conception of matter (relativity, the Heisenberg Principle) and what Mumford calls the "reawakening of the organic," we are moving toward a new basis of culture in which energy flows not so much from machine to society but from society to the machine, through an almost organic route. "The emphasis in the future must be," he writes, "not upon speed and immediate practical conquest, but upon exhaustiveness, inter-relationship, and integration." He compares the old mechanical model with a checkers game, in which all the pieces are qualitatively the same. The cultural or organic impulse, however, is more like chess, where the pieces differ qualitatively, and where each move depends on the position and qualities of all the pieces.

Mumford's argument for an "organic ideology" parallels one of Fuller's central ideas: the establishment of a comprehensive, anticipatory design science. The important distinction is that Mumford stresses a humanistic, organic base, whereas Fuller would follow larger ecological patterns that Mumford himself would probably regard as another imposition of over-rationalistic science upon man.

ON RE-SCALING HISTORY

What Mumford emphasizes in *Technics and Civilization* is the impact that technics have had upon culture. In *The Myth of the Machine* he steps back five millennia to focus on the reverse process: how culture shaped man's early tools and the first of man's machines, the "megamachine."

The Myth of the Machine is a bold book, even for Mumford. In it he challenges not only the current theories of archeologists and prehistorians, but the value of their data, evidence which is, by time's crude selective process, essentially limited to tools and hardware. His tone is brassy and argumentative; he is fighting as strongly against an entrenched position as he is for his own. Yet his evidence and usual ability to bring coherence to far-flung data can be most persuasive.

As early as 1934, Mumford had begun to insist that man is created by his cultural, as opposed to his technical, accomplishments. Mumford's attention to the dynamic interplay between culture and technics (or in later works such as *The Culture of Cities,* between cities and culture) shows his concern for the non-technical underpinnings of culture. His thesis in *The Myth of the Machine* is that the forces that have shaped culture *and technology itself* are not technical but human in origin. Before the hand discovered its versatility, thus awakening the mind, the mind was already awakened, and explored the uses of the hand. Early inventions such as fire, wheel, knife, spear, and bow and arrow sprang from ritual, which is to say from needs larger than simple survival. In short, the great leaps forward in man's history have spiritual rather than technical roots.

Mumford's aim here is not simply to refute textbook interpretations of the chicken-or-egg problem of culture and technics, but to shatter the myth that controls what he calls the "mis-direction" of the twentieth century. We are moving, Mumford believes, toward the age of "megatechnics," where "the dominant minority will create a uniform, all-enveloping, super-planetary structure, designed for automatic operation. Instead of functioning actively as an autonomous personality, man will become a passive, purposeless, machine-conditioned animal, whose proper functions . . . will either be fed into the machine or strictly limited and controlled for the benefit of depersonalized, collective organizations." And man's very image of himself, prehistorically as a tool-making animal, currently as a worker or technician, contributes to and indeed welcomes the coming of megatechnics. *The Myth of the Machine* challenges this image and proposes another. For Mumford, man is not at home in the mechanical environment; he is a being who celebrates, worships, dances, creates, and delights in myths and rituals.

Mumford's arguments are too elaborate to summarize here. Rather I will concentrate on those key points that comprise his distinct contribution to an understanding of technics.

Mumford uses the phrase "technical narcissism" to describe the common bias with which most investigators view the development of early tools. Language, man's most useful early tool, has origins that are probably stronger in dream, myth, and ritual than any other experience. Dreams, for example, must have been among the most vivid experiences of early man. Dreams forced a growing consciousness upon man, and provoked myth, ritual, and the stirrings of imagination and intelligence. Through dreams, rather than tools, man came to yearn for a more expansive and social existence for communication.

Long before he attempted to transform his environment, Mumford asserts, man worked to change himself. The senses had to be trained, the legs tried for speed and power, the arms applied for fighting, gripping, and carrying. Once man discovered his own mind, Mumford claims, he sought, if only dimly, to articulate and develop his potentialities. "Man had to learn to be human, just as he had to learn to talk; and the jump from animalhood to humanhood, definite but gradual and undatable, indeed still unfinished, came through man's endless efforts to shape and re-shape himself." Just what these early feats involved in terms of consciousness and practice we can only surmise; Mumford points to Hindu yoga as a contemporary, far more sophisticated, equivalent.

Early technics, Mumford argues, were the outcome of various cultural forces; the bow and arrow may well have been man's attempt to reconstruct magically the flight of a bird; the development of hunting tools might have had their origin in a growing erotic and masculine consciousness (as, Mumford continues in a Jungian vein, early vessels may have represented the feminine aspect). These are not provable assertions, but Mumford here challenges the tendency to build theories solely on what little evidence remains after the larger structure of cultural life has vanished. Imagine the distorted picture that a future civilization would get if it tried to comprehend the nature of a modern university from its stadium alone.

One of Mumford's most provocative concepts in *The Myth of the Machine* is his definition of the megamachine, and his analysis of the forces that gave rise to it. Neolithic technics were limited to tools; the complex interactions necessary for the machine needed a form to follow, a master blueprint. Mumford sees one where previous historians had never looked: in the organization of a social body created for specialized work. Since the megamachine is not made of metal or wood, Mumford calls it "the invisible machine." Yet its rise in the third millennium B.C. was one of the most distinctive events in the history of technics.

The megamachine was designed and controlled by the emerging power elite of Mesopotamia and the Nile valleys—the kings. With the introduction of the king, a leader of tribes and a man who was part god, a new social organization emerged, one that tended toward an urban-agrarian economy and for which work had to be gradually redefined. Mumford argues with the theorists who claim that the growth of the early cities resulted from technological changes such as writing and the making of metal tools. Behind these new technics lay a force even larger than they. It was the power inherent in social organization, a power hitherto never known by men.

This power is seen most forcefully in the megamachine and its accomplishments. The Great Pyramid, built 3,000 years before Christ, rises almost 500 feet and measures 755 feet square at the base. Its interior contains intricate passageways at different levels, all of which lead finally to the burial chamber. The technical competence with which the blocks of stone were combined (some complex joints were fitted to a thousandth of an inch) would be difficult to equal today. And the original Egyptian megamachine accomplished the task with no power source other than men, no engineering tools beyond the inclined plane and the lever (according to Mumford the wheel was not in use at this time).

To Mumford's way of thinking, the very fact that the Great Pyramid was built proves the existence of the machine. No level of human collaboration alone could have achieved such a task unless the humans involved became rigid, dependable parts of a larger, synchronous machine. One of the essential features of any machine, as Fuller suggests, is that it must be capable of doing more work than the sum of its parts. The discovery that men could form a machine, whether for constructing enormous monuments to their king-gods or for waging war on a new, unprecedented scale, was one of the major steps in the growth of technics and in the development of early civilization.

The step from the megamachine to the machines of the medieval and industrial era was a large, and temporarily interrupted, one, but Mumford argues that it was a step. While the continuation of the idea of the divine authority of kings may have kept it alive, this idea collapsed with the rise of Greek and Roman culture. Christianity provided a religious context drastically different from the Egyptian belief in the divinity of the king. But Christianity provided beliefs and presuppositions that would become the seeding ground for the new technics. "Christianity not merely reconstituted the original forces that were combined in the mega-machine, but added precisely the one element that was lacking: a commitment to moral values and social purposes that transcended the established forms of civilization."

It is no mere irony that the earliest Western machines—the clock, the watermill, the horse-powered treadmill, the windmill—were creations of the monastery. The monastery was Christianity's redefinition of the megamachine; the division of labor, the rigid social organization, and its spiritual motivating force created an institution in which work on a large specialized scale became possible and inevitable. But Christianity gave the new megamachine its distinctive character; work was not the fate of a slave, but a moral choice. By spiritualizing work, the monastery made the necessary step toward freeing it from human hands. In the process the monks discovered that the megamachine was not only a labor-oriented device, but a labor-*saving* device as well, and this insight could be applied to non-human and non-animal energies available. Thus water could be used to rotate the gears that thresh and grind wheat. The megamachine could be viewed as almost all natural or human phenomena were in those times—as a revealed truth whose pattern only needed to be discerned and applied by man.

Mumford provides here an interpretation of the rise of technics in Western culture that differs markedly from his earlier explanation in *Technics and Civilization.* In effect, he is suggesting that technics spring from religious beliefs more than from cultural needs or, indeed, the impetus of their own evolution. This new interpretation, admittedly, is not proved as much as argued through cultural evidence, and it is easy to see how anthropologists and cultural historians might consider it sheer speculation. Yet much of *The Myth of the Machine* could be attacked simply as speculative and ignored. What gives the book its strength is that Mumford seemes to have located a thread that he follows throughout the development of technics, revealing a totally new pattern. Technics, Mumford says, do not as much shape the human condition as respond to it. Man creates the machine, much as he creates art, out of his recognition of who and what he is; it expresses his hopes and his destiny. The great tragedy, the horror we witness today, is man's enthusiasm for fashioning technics out of a twisted belief that they can change him for the better. To forget that man is the wellspring of technics is to forget one's own humanity. And that, for Mumford, is the worst kind of betrayal.

MUMFORD'S DILEMMA

"Nothing produced by technics is more final than the human needs and interests themselves that have created technics." At the center of the spiraling process of man and his technologies is man. And for Mumford no changes in the external environment can be so profound, or can warrant the study of the unchanging quality which is man—his sense of himself, his needs, his ambitions. Only with our eyes on the human needs and ambitions that have given rise to technics, suggests Mumford, can we rightly perceive the technics. It is all a matter of perspective.

The humanistic perspective is at once Mumford's genius and his pitfall. By stressing persistence over change, he has shown the panoply of technical innovations somewhat as shifts in geological strata over a vast terrain. But the terrain, however much its topography has been altered, remains the same place, resting on the same rock. Mumford has made man the unchanging principle against the flux of environmental change. But in doing so he has inadvertently set man against the machine. Implicit in this perspective, however, is a basic attitude toward man and his technologies: that no matter how much environments change, man remains essentially the same. Mumford refuses to allow that the threshold of change, the degree to which technologies can indeed change man, can reach and affect man as a species. The idea of some sort of technological or cultural evolution *of the species* thus remains alien to Mumford. Moreover, Mumford gives no basis for suggesting that technologies may reach a stage where the ways in which they change man become fundamentally different from the processes observable in previous history. Fresh technics can be "new," but the ways in which they reshape culture and personality cannot.

What is Lewis Mumford's contribution to a field theory of

man's relationship to his technologies? Two questions can be raised here. First, precisely how does Mumford define the man-environment relationship? Second, does he posit a technological determinism, and if so, to what extent?

Each of the men who are featured in this book tends to focus the interaction between technology and man upon one aspect of man and society. Innis, for example, follows the media of communication to the social institutions that they create; McLuhan concentrates on the sensory ratios and their effects. Such focus is a major aspect of each man's conception of the interplay between man and his environment. In Mumford, the focus is usually quite broad. In discussing the role of war in producing the military engineer, he reveals the cross-currents of technics and culture that create a new social organization—in this case, the development of the army as a mechanical system. In one chapter he discusses the rise of romanticism as a reaction to the industrialization of life—the emotional focus. In another he suggests the motion picture as shifting the perception of space and time—the sensory focus. If there is any principal focus of this sort in Mumford, it is with the somewhat nebulous area of "personality."

Throughout *Technics and Civilization,* and to a lesser extent in other works, Mumford displays a fascination with the "personality types" who created and in turn were influenced by modern technics. He distinguishes between the cautious, conservationist woodsman and the miner, who feels no guilt in ruining the land. Tenth-century man was subjectively conditioned, whereas contemporary man is objectively conditioned. A man of the eotechnic phase directed his loyalty to kin, tribe, nation; man today is loyal to abstractions disguised as facts. The contrasts abound, and the references serve as signposts of change along the way. Indeed, Mumford likes to describe a type of personality produced by a particular technical era, then to swing around and redefine that era in terms of the personality type he has just described. Thus modern man, with his belief in objective data, represents the triumph of a neutral, objective world over the subjective or theologically objective world of the past.

For Mumford the relationship between man and his technics is largely one of projection and reaction. Man, extending a single need or function into the environment, tends to surround himself with reminders of that need, and thereby somehow loses an earlier wholeness, dislocating himself. Mumford expresses it succinctly: "In projecting one side of the human personality into the concrete forms of the machine, we have created an independent environment that has reacted upon every other side of the personality."

Mumford views the relationship between man and his mechanized environment as a fundamental tension between the organic and the inorganic, a sociological extension of the problem of primitive biological friction. Here again Mumford is drawing on his teacher, Patrick Geddes, who stated that man must design his environment to reflect the deeper, unconscious energies and vitalities that bind him to nature. Mumford sees the great threat of the machine in its inducement for man to deny the organic, to acquiesce to the rationalistic and institutionalizing demands of technics.

The concept of technological determinism applies less to Mumford than to anyone else in this section. By his insistence that man is always at the controls of his technics—or responsible for the abdication of those controls—Mumford has set himself apart from Ellul, who posits a distinct and fearful determinism, and Giedion, who implies a determinism in the center of the process of mechanization. True enough, Mumford likens our present condition to the passengers of a runaway locomotive. But he places the blame squarely on man, and insists that we are at fault for ever accelerating without enough knowledge of the controls.

There is no doubt that Mumford sees the machine as endangering man. His remark on the spectre of a "uniform, planetary, all-enveloping structure," in *The Myth of the Machine* suggests his alarm at the current state of technics and man's growing subservience to them. *Art and Technics* addresses precisely this problem. Mumford rebukes those who say that we must "adapt" to the demands of the machine, that we must bring our morality and social behavior up to the level required by the new worldwide ecology (W. F. Ogburn's "cultural lag," for example, or Buckminster Fuller's argument about war). He claims, rather, that we have overdeveloped our technics; it is not a problem of behavior failing to keep up with technology, but of letting it get so that we think that way. The machine thereby becomes the norm, and human behavior, cultural lag or not, is forced to adjust to it. The very idea of the machine rather than man being the norm horrifies Mumford.

But why cannot technics take the lead in cultural evolution? Why must man invariably be the decisive factor? Is there no possibility of a kind of serendipity in cultural change, or does Mumford, like Ellul, believe that the machine as such is contagiously evil? Here the unique Mumfordian balance of romanticism and historical perspective adjusts the problem to its potential solution. Thus, in *Art and Technics,* he pleads for an allegiance between the technician and the designer, the scientist and the artist. The machine, indeed, is the pathway to a new aesthetic crowned by the virtues of precision, calculation, flawlessness, clarity, simplicity, and economy. Each new machine offers wider possibilities. "Though it has been so stupidly misused, the motion picture nevertheless announces itself as a major art of the neotechnic phase. Through the machine, we have new possibilities of understanding the world we have helped to create."

Yet on a closer look we see that Mumford has trapped

himself in his own argument. The very danger he fears, that the machine will become the precursor of culture, is heralded in the context of aesthetics. But cannot a technological aesthetic dehumanize man as well? Norman Mailer's complaint about modern architecture shows the precariousness of Mumford's conclusions. Even the most innovative buildings, Mailer states, remain straight and spatially vacuous. Where are the hidden recesses, the shadowy places, the leering gargoyles, the fanciful intricacies of other eras? If architecture or, indeed, all modern technics are somehow to suggest the range of man's experience, do not shame, secrecy, fear, and dread deserve an external face?

Finally, Mumford's contribution to an understanding of the technological situation cannot be evaluated on the basis of questions of determinism or the relationship between technology and man. As a cultural historian and a very notable one, Mumford has provided a view of history that succeeds, within its own framework, in exploring the interconnections between technics and culture. By locating the lines of stress of any period running between the technology and its cultural context, he has shown how the stresses result in new social configurations that themselves give rise to new technologies. There is no question that Mumford is highly adept at working with the past, and in seeing it whole, stretched across its vast expanse. But the question that arises here, and the question that overshadows Mumford's work, is whether the process of technical social change as he interprets it is helpful when one approaches the drastically new technics of the twentieth century.

This is not to suggest that the complex of electronic technologies that typify the twentieth century somehow defy history, but simply that the best of Mumford's analysis works from categories drawn from periods before the twentieth century, perhaps, as a valid historical method, necessarily so. The problem is one of scope. To what extent are these categories and interpretations capable of relating to the new phenomena? Can atomic energy accurately be compared with the steam engine, or plastics with wood and iron? Are there not more substantial differences that outweigh the similarities? Does the real significance of the new communications—one of Mumford's most striking weaknesses—lie in new systems of recording information, or in new ecologies of information, that would require a work of a totally different scale and approach than that to which Mumford can relate historically? These questions are aimed at a larger problem than Mumford's inadequate description of the neotechnic era. Mumford's very contribution to a total environmental science hinges largely on the applicability of his categories and insights to the present dilemma. The historian need not *be* a prophet, but he should supply the stuff for prophets. Has Mumford done so?

The critical irony in Mumford's work, what one might call "Mumford's dilemma," is that his focus on history, and particularly on the sources of continuity in history, have isolated him from the very process he has studied and conveyed so thoroughly. He has failed to locate in the past the determinants that have become so overwhelmingly powerful in the present. And this leaves his humanism, too, somewhat anachronistic. Mumford has shown us the guidelines to the ecological foundations of major periods in the past, how they were shaped, and how they in turn reshaped further periods. Yet when applied to the present, these guidelines no longer provide guidance. Is the weakness in his guidelines, or has the twentieth century been more disruptive and revolutionary than anything history might have led him to suspect?

Perhaps Mumford's dilemma is characterized best by one of his own images: the cultural pseudomorph. Like a rock that retains its shape but loses its substance, the historian very well might approach the present with the forms (neotechnic phase, energy and pace, substance and consciousness) that fitted the phenomena of the past so well. But if somehow the intrinsic substance of the phenomena have changed, does the rock retain its own identity—does the historian retain his worth?

Any historical approach to today's technological phenomena involves risk. And the risk is worth running because we need as never before to understand the interaction of the forces at work when a new technology (or a new onslaught of technologies) is introduced into a culture. The difficulty Mumford raises is to show that these forces may not be understood aright if we read the record of the past only from an excursion into the past. The present, as never before, is the proper vantage point of history; and sadly, it is a present at which one of our best historians has stood too briefly, too precariously, and too glumly.

FOUR

The Nuts and Bolts of History *Are* History

SIEGFRIED GIEDION

The relations between man and his environment are subject to continual and restless change; from generation to generation, from year to year, from instant to instant, they are in danger of losing their equilibrium. There is no static equilibrium between man and his environment, between inner and outer reality.

Siegfried Giedion,
Mechanization Takes Command

At first glance, *Mechanization Takes Command* seems less a history of the impact of technics upon nineteenth-century America than a grand catalog of machines and gadgets, furniture and bathtubs. Giedion's copious illustrations and his concentration on technical data give the book a flavor of the 1890 Sears Roebuck catalog interspersed with a technical manual on the operation and repair of the devices it displays. Yet the book presents a concentrated history of the most important period in mechanization. And lodged beneath the seemingly objective processes that Giedion chronicles so thoroughly lies a theory of technology that deserves attention.

Giedion's background and reputation lie not in technics but architecture. His *Space, Time and Architecture* has established him as a major historian of the modern period. It has also done much to promote his unique approach to architectural history—as the interaction between sensory biases and spatial configurations. As will be shown in Chapter Seven, Giedion along with Wyndham Lewis and Harold Innis anticipated much of McLuhan and contributed significantly to his most important thought.

The subtitle for *Mechanization Takes Command* is, "A Contribution to Anonymous History"—which characterizes not only its content, but its manner. In preparing the book Giedion spent several years stalking the archives of older industries and poring over what records remain at places such as the U.S. Patent Office. Whereas Mumford was content to describe and interpret the major innovations in technics over a period of almost a thousand years, Giedion has concentrated almost entirely upon specific technologies within the nineteenth century. He limits his focus to America. "The process leading up to the present role of mechanization can nowhere be observed better than in the United States, where the new methods of production were first applied, and where mechanization is inextricably woven into the pattern of thought and customs."

The specialized focus serves him well. Rather than attempt the larger cultural schemata of Mumford, Giedion can distinguish the exact steps taken in the mechanization of hog slaughter and pork packing, showing at first hand the confrontation between the mechanical and the organic; or the mechanization of the bath, revealing how regeneration is transformed—partly through the introduction of technology—into a simple hygienic function. He has written what appears to be a catalog history of various mechanical forms; it reaches, however, into the precise and often subtle transformations that mechanization creates.

Siegfried Giedion's method follows the European model,

particularly the historical school of Jakob Burkhardt, his teacher. Burkhardt emphasized sources and records, particularly those of unseemly value that had been ignored by other historians, and discouraged too great a role for opinion. Giedion not only brings together a density of factual material, but draws it from every source conceivable: patent registrations, original pamphlets and catalogs, nineteenth-century journals and records. Even his organization of the book follows the strictest line of evidence, concentrating on particular technologies such as the assembly line, the changes in furniture design, refrigeration, and streamlining. Anonymous history requires at least the face of its progress, assumes Giedion, to be understood aright.

It is important to understand precisely what Giedion means by "anonymous history," for his interpretation of technics in human society differs in several important ways from that of Mumford. "The slow shaping of daily life is of equal importance to the explosions of history," he writes, "for, in the anonymous life, the particles accumulate into an explosive force. Tools and objects are outgrowths of fundamental attitudes to the world. These attitudes set the course followed by thought and action." In effect, anonymous history is invisible history. Giedion uses the metaphor of the magnetic lines of force that exist within a pattern of magnets. A handful of iron filings will become a design revealing those lines of force. "So, too, the details of anonymous history can be made to reveal the meaning of a period."

Giedion's history is therefore a study of fragments in their relationship to the whole. In conception, method, and to a certain extent in conclusions, this puts Giedion at a distinct remove from Mumford. Mumford moves through history by quantum jumps, showing how major technics reflect and project themselves into an era. Giedion follows a slower, more restrained pace, preferring the seemingly minor technics to the major ones (in Giedion there is nothing about the steam engine or the evolution of the internal combustion engine). Mumford's writings follow the total cultural flow, whereas Giedion's cultural observations emerge almost totally from the impact of a distinct mechanical innovation. Mumford organizes his data around large-scale trends (the three phases of technics are good examples, though not the only ones); Giedion's organization is strictly typological, focusing upon certain areas of mechanization ("Mechanization Encounters the Organic," "Mechanization Encounters the Household") and, within each of these, following the development of the major technologies through the nineteenth and into the twentieth century.

Giedion differs somewhat from Mumford in the themes that dominate his work. The encounter between mechanization and the organic, for example, is Giedion's counterpart to the Geddes-Mumford motif of the organic-inorganic friction that underlies man's relationship to a technological environment. Giedion approaches the problem within its original setting, however, showing how the processes of organization and production have affected agricultural practices, the packing of meat, the making of bread. Where Geddes and Mumford look to biological models, Giedion looks to history.

Giedion differs from Mumford in his approach to change. If constancy underlies the change effected by technology in Mumford, the process is reversed in Giedion: here constancy is undermined by change. Indeed, the final and most important theme in Giedion, the growth of the split between thought and feeling, is itself a measure of the ravages of this change upon man.

There can be no question that, besides Mumford, Giedion is the major historian of technics. Indeed, the two complement one another; Mumford emphasizing the historical context, Giedion concentrating on the elaborate, painstaking process by which a distinct aspect of life becomes increasingly mechanized in recent history.

The approach taken in this chapter will be to focus on three areas of mechanization that Giedion describes: movement, the encounter between the machine and organic substances, and the bath. Rather than attempt a summary of each of these areas—a task made nearly impossible by Giedion's range and scale—I will focus on the most symptomatic developments, to suggest what Giedion has done with them.

THE ORGANIZATION OF MOVEMENT

In Mumford's work, the central thrust of technics can be seen in its energy sources and energy levels: from water and wind to coal to electricity. Significantly, Giedion says next to nothing of energy but concentrates instead on what to him is the most symptomatic feature of mechanization: movement. The contrast between the regular, synchronous movements of the machine and the more erratic, spontaneous movements of organic life recurs through *Mechanization Takes Command* as a dominant motif. Thus for Giedion the assembly line is implicitly more important than the steam engine; the motion studies and time-work research of figures like Marey and Gilbreth and Taylor is more important to him than discoveries in mining or the internal combustion engine. The movement of machine characteristics into man's body and consciousness reveals mechanization at its most profound level.

Giedion approaches the phenomenon from two viewpoints: historical attitudes toward, and studies of, movement (the theoretical approach), and the growth of the assembly line and scientific management (the industrial approach). Each viewpoint reflects a distinct trend toward quantifying the movements of man, making them accessible and rhythmically organized to the movements of the machine.

Movement, Giedion notes, is a phenomenon to which both the Greeks and medievals directed only cursory attention. Not until the fourteenth century did anyone, notably Nicholas Oresme, attempt to represent movement graphically: the first step toward a valid method of measuring and understanding physical movement. Despite some work during and after the Renaissance, the real impetus came in the nineteenth century with the French physiologist Étienne Marey (1830-1904). In 1860 Marey invented the Spygmograph, which recorded the form and frequency of the human heartbeat. Later devices gave the Spygmograph the added sophistication necessary to record graphically movements inside the body (blood flow, muscular interaction) and of moving bodies (the gait of a horse, the flights of insects and birds). In the 1880s Marey turned to the camera, and developed his "photographic gun," which took distinct photographs at small intervals, one of the important ancestors of the motion picture camera. In all his studies, Marey attempted to project the flow of movement beyond the physical form: to chart pure movement rather than study the distinctive movement within a body.

Frank B. Gilbreth (1868-1924) took Marey's work further, concentrating on the movements of the human body, and attempting its precise visualization in time and space. Whereas Marey's trajectories seem simplifications of movement, Gilbreth's cyclograph reveals a far more complex world of movement, in which the time-space intervals are recorded as bold, original scrawls on a sheet.

Such studies, Giedion suggests, both influenced and reflected the consciousness of an epoch. He sees parallels to such studies in art, in Bergson's lectures, in Joyce's experimentation with language. And he asks the question, "Are the trajectories, as recorded by a production engineer, 'to eliminate needless, ill-directed, ineffective motion,' in any way connected with the emotional impact of the signs that appear time and again in our contemporary art?" The emotional roots of art may, through conquest of mechanization, give way to newer ones—roots that emerge from the mechanized culture itself.

The studies of Marey and Gilbreth only underscore the tendency toward comprehending and controlling motion for its productive uses. Mechanization *is* movement, the distinct and precise movements of machines; and their consistent, mechanical nature tends to change everything they contact—including the workers on assembly lines.

The assembly line, Giedion notes, did not begin with Henry Ford, but in a forgotten pork-packing plant in Cincinnati in the early 1830s. Earlier steps had led to this point: the interchangeability of parts (attributed to Eli Whitney in gun manufacture), the specialization of work functions, the newer methods of pressing, stamping, and die casting. The original assembly lines were barely more than elaborate conveyor systems, with workers doing specialist's tasks along the line. But by 1900 management was concentrating on ways of improving production *within* the plant, and it was only natural that they should turn to the problem of organization of work—the essential feature of the assembly line.

Giedion equates the growth of the assembly line with the development of scientific management; both use the same tools, both aim at uninterrupted production process; both work toward integrating the factory into a "single tool where all the phases of production, all the machines, become one great unit."

The name of Frederick Winslow Taylor (1856-1915) dominates the early history of scientific management. Taylor directed time studies aimed at improving efficiency, but he always worked within the context of total organizational flow. The human body is studied for both forms of ease in work, and for the points at which it can be most rigorously adapted to the rhythms and demands of the machine. The lines of stress, the limits of force, and the ultimate aim of greater efficiency dominated all Taylor's work—whether his managerial theories or his construction of a new tensile steel. He identified, and enabled a generation of management to identify, human work with mechanical efficiency. He conceived the factory as a closed organism, with each worker and each machine serving a specialized function. He prepared, as Giedion observes, the alliance between scientific management and experimental psychology—an alliance that would eventually give added sophistication and added authority to his formulations. Frank Gilbreth continued this tradition, going from the stage of the stop watch to a total reorganization of work processes and tempo based around the single question, "How long does it take to do a piece of work?" Gilbreth went beyond the work of Marey and defined his own lines of movement, trying to find how the movements and tempo of the human body could best adapt to those of the machine. Can a bricklayer work faster if he lifts the brick, or simply reaches across for it? By constructing wire models of various work functions, Gilbreth attempted to make management and workers what he called "motion-minded."

"It is not surprising," Giedion comments upon Gilbreth, that the trajectories of bodily movement "should become for him entities with independent laws." Gilbreth brought movement studies into the twentieth century, not only by making management conscious of the possibilities they created for speeding up production, but likewise in expressing movement *in time*: not through successive stages, as Marey and Muybridge had done, but within the clear sweep of a simple motion recorded in time. Giedion shows how these two periods operated in art, with the successive phase stage represented by the Italian Futurists and the early cubists (the perfect example, of course, is Marcel Duchamp's "Nude Descending a Staircase") and the latter phase of pure movement reflected in the work of Dadaists, surrealists, and contemporary artists such as Joan Miro and Paul Klee. Giedion suggests the emergence of a third stage in both art and motion studies, in which "the form of movement becomes a means of expression in painting just as perspective had formerly been the means of expressing a specific content, an isolated scene." (This concept has been developed in a number of ways in György Kepes's volume *The Nature and Art of Motion.*)

The growth of the assembly line in the twentieth century had moved increasingly toward "pure mechanization," the process reached when the machine does all the work, and man serves only as a guardian of its processes—in effect, automation. By the end of the 1920s the automatic assembly line was introduced for the construction of automobile frames in Milwaukee; since then it has come to dominate many industries where the product is non-organic and so oriented to standardization that human work would be crippling rather than advantageous.

The process of mechanizing movement has, Giedion states, achieved two important effects: the quantification of human movement (thereby making man adjustable to the machine) and the decisive, perhaps irreversible, trend of production efficiency over human rhythms, needs, and styles. Man increasingly moves less by the measure of his own body and mind than by that of the machine.

WHAT HAPPENED TO BREAD?

For Giedion, mechanization is much like Ellul's "technique": an unkind Midas that transforms everything it touches. The range of this transformation and its visible by-products are thoroughly apparent in the process whereby wheat threshing, storing, dough preparation, and bread baking and packaging become mechanized. Giedion's description of the process in the mechanization of bread reads with the chilling authority of a well-told horror story.

In many ways the story of the mechanization of bread tells the larger story of the mechanization of society. As Giedion writes, "If man deviates too long from the constant of nature, his taste becomes slowly vitiated and his whole organism threatened. Unwittingly, he impairs judgment and instinct, without which balance is so easily lost." Bread, closer to man than most products of mechanization, is not so close as it was before the machine. What happened to bread?

The earliest attempt to mechanize bread production (as distinct from flour milling, which goes back to the tenth century) lay in the efforts to free men from the chore of kneading the dough—the most onerous step of bread baking, as it involves pulling, pushing, and beating. Various kneading implements have been used since Roman times, all of which helped human effort, but did not improve upon kneading by hand. Early in the nineteenth century new innovations sprang up in France that still used human energy (a rotating wheel), but that could successfully imitate the movements of the human hand. By the turn of the century the new machines no longer tried to imitate the human hand, but were directed toward a different principle—churning, or in the case of the high-speed mixer, agitation. The high-speed mixer is especially important here, because it has come to control the kneading process in bread-making. The great advantage of the high-speed mixer is that it guarantees a uniform structure to the dough. The disadvantage is that its speed of operation accelerates so quickly that the shock destroys all but the hardiest wheats, thereby making the bread of the more delicate European wheats unavailable in the common market.

Until the seventeenth century, baking ovens for bread tended to be egg-shaped, built to best retain and distribute heat uniformly. Such an oven might serve personal bread-making needs, but resisted mechanization. Improved ovens, such as the indirectly heated oven, were tried, and by the middle of the nineteenth century the principle of the endless belt running through a large oven had been established. The twin urge toward a continuously running mechanism and cutting down the time necessary for baking dominated efforts throughout the last half of the nineteenth century. Only after 1915, when gas supplanted coal heating, did the principle of high-pressure steam become common—insuring both accurately controlled and evenly distributed heat. Baking time was cut down to one quarter. This raised other problems, particularly in the leavening; but there were new answers to these.

Traditionally dough was mixed with leaven for tastiness, rising, and bread's porous quality. Leaven, however, is a slow-working ferment; it takes several hours to bake properly. Mechanization demands speed above all, and the need for a new leavening material became apparent through the latter part of the nineteenth century. Brewer's yeast was tried first, then carbonic acid, eventually a range of chemicals. Not only did yeast hasten the baking process, experimenters discovered, but the introduction of various gases gave the illusion of taller bread, whiter bread, tastier bread. Indeed, the weight of a loaf could be cut down by half if enough gas was introduced, yet the size would be greater; need bread be heavy if it can be big? Soda water, baking powder, and carbonic acid were used for brief periods late in the nineteenth century. Eventually more satisfactory chemicals—including water, fats, sugar, vitamins

—were introduced, either as gases or through the hypodermic principle at the dough stage.

Mechanization not only affects the bread-making process; it reaches back and reshapes the flour. Earlier milling processes had resulted in a wheat mixture that contained not only the grain, but the oily germ—the embryo of future stalks, and therefore a vitamin-rich property. As production increased, and the demand for "quality flour" (usually meaning white and non-oily flour) grew, a new milling process became popular. Instead of grinding the wheat with slight unevenness and permitting it to age for several months to achieve its final color, the new process ground the wheat thoroughly, destroying the germ in the process. Through high-voltage currents or the uses of gases like chlorine, it became a chemical more than a natural product. "Mechanization of the milling process," Giedion writes, "yielded a brilliant façade and a more or less artificial product. The oleaginous germ that formerly made the flour somewhat greasy to the touch, and which contains the valuable elements, has been rigorously excluded."

Full mechanization of the bread-making process became possible only in the twentieth century. The use of chemically changed flour, the addition of artificially introduced gases and vitamins, the mechanical kneading and quick-baking process, all became rigidly standardized, guaranteeing uniform loaves of bread with uniform density, size, and weight. Giedion points to a curious phenomenon here: the interaction between mechanized production and public taste. Mechanization tends toward a frothy, white, soft bread. Not only did public taste accept these features, but eagerly accepted "improved," accentuated versions of these qualities. Public taste is reflected and created by mechanization. Bread may be only partially baked, stripped of its organic vitamins, and blown up by artificially added chemicals, but its continuation is guaranteed by the very process that led to its introduction: mechanization.

OF BATHTUBS AND THE MACHINE

Mechanization standardized products, reshaping the environment. But more subtly, it altered the inner qualities of things—whether a loaf of bread or the life span of an automobile. What happens when mechanization encounters the most primitive of personal and social customs, such as the bath?

Giedion sees two great historical meanings in the bath: care of the body ("external ablution") and total regeneration, or a kind of spiritual renewal. Within Western culture, a bath can be traced back to the Greeks, where it was an adjunct to the gymnasium, a link between sport and philosophical discussion. Whereas the Greek bath involved cold showers and ablutions and was simply performed, the later Roman baths grew to enormous proportions. Floors and walls were heated; the originally personal character of the bath became distinctly social. What began originally as a brief form of regeneration became in Roman culture a major social event. The regeneration principle had not disappeared, but took on a new shape: Romans using the baths would exercise in the palestra, spend time in the warm tepidarium, move into the laconicum, where hot dry air whipped the body to endurance in minutes, and after soaping and massage would enter the frigid waters of the pool.

The development of the bath in Western society has followed the Roman, more than the Greek, concept of regeneration, though never would the bath again reach the level of institutionalization that it had possessed in Rome. In the latter part of the medieval period the steam bath came into Europe from Finland and Russia, reviving the social dimension of bathing. But this very revival, Giedion notes, led to the decay of regeneration. The baths of the middle ages are depicted in the paintings of that period with an erotic tinge, and by the time of the Reformation and the Counter-Reformation, social forms of bathing disappeared in Europe. In the seventeenth and early eighteenth centuries bathing became infrequent; indeed, it was allied with sin. Only with the medical advances of the eighteenth century and the return to nature typified by Rousseau did bathing reappear, though for its specifically hygienic rather than regenerative value.

Until the nineteenth century, mechanization had barely affected the development of the bath: its sources were primarily cultural. Despite efforts toward the social bathhouse and the total regeneration that accompanied it, mechanization moved toward the private shower and bathtub. New discoveries, such as hydrotherapy and the vapor bath, became immediately mechanized and were marketed individually, since no social market usually existed. The irony underlying the innovations in baths in the latter half of the nineteenth century was that a strong trend of man "returning to nature" through the bath was joined to the mechanical production of bathing facilities. Increasingly different kinds of bath were invented, but except within institutional contexts (such as miners' cabins) they were individualized and purely functional—inhibiting the natural regenerative tendency of the bath. By the end of the nineteenth century the totally functional bathroom became common in houses and apartments. Here ruling tastes in style became more important than mechanical innovations; indeed, as Giedion notes, the mechanisms operating twentieth-century baths are actually quite primitive.

Bathing can be a form of ablution, or a regeneration, or both. Usually when it becomes a private matter, its ablution quality dominates. Social bathing tends toward regeneration. Mechanization did not kill the regenerative bath, Giedion says, but it has successfully resisted its return.

AN END TO MECHANIZATION?

"Mechanization," Giedion writes, "is the outcome of a mechanistic conception of the world, just as technique is the outcome of science." The image of the world brought about by the Newtonian revolution and the seventeenth-century savants has found its final impact in a world-spanning complex of mechanistic technologies. But mechanization, Giedion argues, cannot forever build upon itself: the edifice rests on a fragile base, human needs. This base can shift, permitting the whole to corrode and topple.

Giedion's history of mechanization is a study of the forest through the qualities of its trees. He avoids the larger judgments that a cultural approach such as Mumford's demands; likewise, he is able to give a more direct and explicit glimpse of the process of mechanical evolution. In trying to interpret the meaning of his work for the larger problem of technology, several factors must be taken into account. Giedion's history presents only certain aspects of mechanization: notably the assembly line, particular agricultural and food-preparing developments, furniture, kitchen and home appliances, the bath. He ignores most industrial developments and, significantly, all forms of weaponry. His catalog, then, is a very incomplete one; Giedion has only chosen a small group of trees for his study.

Likewise, Giedion's focus on the nineteenth century makes his use of the term "mechanization" quite distinct from Mumford's broader "technics." Mechanization is the process of the machine's evolution within society, and the machine here is the nineteenth-century model, an ensemble of moving parts that does a particular kind of work. Technics can include electronic technologies; mechanization implicitly does not. Giedion's history therefore must be viewed entirely within its nineteenth-century context. The machine acts upon man by controlling his movement, by altering the configurations of his environment, by subtly reshaping his needs. The later impact of electronics would usher in a drastically new mode of interaction, hinted at by Mumford, given further development by Ellul, and more thoroughly explored by Wiener and McLuhan.

Giedion's historical analysis is so deeply rooted in its sources, and organized so objectively, that the question of technological determinism does not impose itself directly upon his conclusions. "We have refrained," he writes in the concluding chapter, "from taking a positive stand for or against mechanization. We cannot simply approve or disapprove. One must discriminate between those spheres that are fit for mechanization and those that are not; similar problems arise today in whatever sphere we touch."

The dangers of mechanization are increasingly present, he acknowledges; but they can be routed only by the rediscovery of what he calls "dynamic equilibrium"—a new balance between the mind and the feelings, between the inner and outer worlds of man. A drastic transformation of man's external environment triggers a chain reaction of modifications in his own organic life of thought, feeling, and bodily activity. The great threat of mechanization lies not in the external environment, but in man's hesitation to respond actively, to change himself and thereby avoid being acted upon as a passive agent.

It is interesting that, while Giedion's view of mechanization is less deterministic than Mumford's, the major determinist among technological theorists, Jacques Ellul, would find Giedion much more useful than Mumford. The reason is clear enough: Mumford constructs the history of technics within and against a humanist culture; Giedion presents mechanization as the cause and causeway of the transformations of society. Ellul's thesis is not a counterpart to Giedion's work, but an elaborate philosophical construction with Giedion's historical data used for important building blocks. Whether or not Giedion would agree with the directions in which Ellul takes his work is altogether another question.

FIVE

A New Manichaeism?

JACQUES ELLUL

> If we desire to preserve man's freedom, dignity and responsibility, it is precluded to act upon him by technical means, like psychology. . . . To transform a man into a reasonable being and a good exploiter of techniques through certain psychological procedures is precisely to destroy him as a spiritual and ethical subject.
>
> Jacques Ellul,
> "The Technological Order"

In the work of Mumford and Giedion, technics and mechanization appear as the central factors in the rise of technology. History (Giedion's "anonymous history") changes when the hard, external things change, when iron replaces wood, and coal power replaces water power; when men move from the farms into the coal mines, or from the mines into the new, brightly lit factories. Technology shapes the context of life, and as the contexts change, men and their culture change. It is an indirect, almost a happenstance process. And if technology fails to alleviate misery, but only compounds it, as was the case in the industrialized nations of the nineteenth century, the blame falls not on the tools, which are in themselves neutral, but upon historical circumstances, economic conditions, and the inability of men to anticipate the drastic patterns that a new technology creates.

Jacques Ellul's major work, *The Technological Society,* cuts violently against the grain of such thinking, viewing technology as a far more awesome and inexplicable phenomenon than either Mumford or Giedion suggest. For Ellul, Mumford's analysis reveals the limited focus of a specialist, and therefore it can serve no further than to catalogue obvious historical developments. He is kinder to Giedion, but only because Giedion's description of "mechanization" comes closer to Ellul's own conception of "technique." Ellul has drawn from Mumford's and Giedion's source material, but only to transcend it by redefining the technological environment as an incredible force with its own autonomous mandate and capacity to transform every sector of human life into its own terms. Ellul's vision is best symbolized by Dr. Frankenstein's monster, which, once alive, cannot be killed, coped with, related to, or compromised. Except that as Ellul tells it, the monster also has the supreme advantage of invisibility. And not seeing him, people refuse to believe that he roams their world.

Jacques Ellul is a curious candidate for prophet. Born in 1912 in Bordeaux, France, he took his baccalaureate in theology and his doctorate in the history of law and social science. For several years he taught at the University of Strausbourg, and in 1938 became a professor of sociology and history of law at the University of Bordeaux, where he has taught since. In World War II he worked in the resistance movement during the Nazi-sponsored Vichy regime, and upon the liberation of Bordeaux was awarded a political post, assistant to the mayor. His important writings consist of three books with enough cohesion of theme and structure to constitute a trilogy: *La Technique,* translated as *The Technological Society* (1954), *Propaganda* (1962), and *The Political Illusion* (1965). He has since written a sometimes scathing, often witty, group of essays, *A Critique of the New Commonplaces* (1968).

Ellul's writings also include a collection of smaller, more polemical books centered on problems of Christianity and ethics. His emphatic and somewhat quixotic Calvinism can be seen in all of them: *The Theological Foundations of Law* (1946), *The Presence of the Kingdom* (1948), *Violence* (1968), and *To Will and To Do* (1969). Indeed, the determinism, the unflagging idealism, and the somber, urgent mood of *The Technological Society* have more than a little to do with his stance as a militant Christian Calvinist. The Ellul who decries a secularization of Christianity in *The Presence of the Kingdom* is the same man who posits an irreconcilable conflict between technique and the vital sources of human life in *The Technological Society*. While it would be exaggerating to claim that Ellul has extrapolated Calvin's doctrine of predestination from the theological into the sociological sphere, there can be little question that Ellul's staunch Calvinism has profoundly affected his sociology, giving it a moral urgency and a tone of authority found rarely among European sociologists.

Of all the subjects he has treated, sociologically or theologically, none have received the attention or the development that Ellul gives to the technological phenomenon. *The Technological Society* is not simply Ellul's best book. It remains to this date the only comprehensive treatment of modern technology as a distinct and unique phenomenon in the history of man. By identifying a single force at the center of technology, Ellul analyzes that force, locates its emergence from history, interprets its range and power, and follows its repercussions into every segment of life: economics, politics, law, education, religion, eating habits, work, recreation. The book moves forward with an ineluctable singleness of purpose and clarity of design absent in Giedion's meticulous scholarship and Mumford's attention to the cultural context.

Technics and Civilization and *Mechanization Takes Command* are historial. Their purpose is not as much to prove a thesis as to interpret the historical development of a phenomenon. *The Technological Society* falls between sociology and philosophy. The subject and thrust are sociological, but the method is phenomenological. Ellul uses data, both historical and sociological in origin, less as the clues to a pattern than as the artillery in his mounted offensive upon the reader. Ellul intends above all to make a point; the erudite, comprehensive scholar may well have in him the soul of a preacher.

Ellul's phenomenology may be exhaustive; perhaps largely for that very reason it is intensely critical and so darkly shaded as to seem fatalistic. The word "pessimist" springs to mind when reading or discussing Ellul, and seems to fit no critic of technology quite as well as him. No man likes to be called a pessimist, and Ellul has countered the label by saying that he is not making value judgments; he is simply diagnosing an ailment. But his judgment runs all the deeper if his very conception of the technological phenomenon begins, to use his metaphor, as a disease.

Ellul has never received the popularity in America, or in England or France, for that matter, that has been accorded other prophets of technological change such as McLuhan or Buckminster Fuller. Part of the reason lies in Ellul's pessimism, that can be as infectious to his readers as Fuller's enthusiasm, but considerably less cheering. Another reason may be seen in Ellul's writings themselves, which are long and repetitious, moving with the inexorable pace of some gigantic, lumbering beast. Yet Ellul's analysis and criticisms deserve to be heard. What many writers, artists, and filmmakers insinuate, and what much of our contemporary experience suggests—that technology is somehow reshaping our institutions and our personalities in ways that we cannot quite yet perceive—Ellul has explored thoroughly and pressed to its ultimate, frightening conclusion. Political commentators, for example, discuss how television has transformed American politics; Ellul goes further, insisting that technique undermines any political system and establishes its own unique totalitarianism. In effect, technique becomes for Ellul the religion, the ideology, and the central force of our society. Yet the man's vision cannot be ignored. No matter how starkly he depicts modern society at the mercy of technique, his description is too perceptive, too bold, and too convincing to be ignored.

TECHNIQUE AS HERO

Perhaps nowhere can Ellul's concept of technique be seen so graphically as in the television series "Mission: Impossible." Ostensibly a spy series, the episodes follow feats of technical virtuosity. In the process people are seen as highly competent technicians; the scale becomes that of the machine and man's interaction with it, and technique emerges as the only hero.

The plots build essentially around the various gadgets and deceptions that the Impossible Missions Force (IMF) frames. In one episode, for example, the IMF must ensure that the money kept in a casino vault will not be spent on the weapons designated for a civil war. To avert this, they use an elaborate complex of devices, including a miniaturized computer that can be worn inside a vest, to win money at the gaming tables and to steal it from the vault. In every plot, the technically conceived plan, a precise blueprint of what the IMF will do, functions as smoothly as a General Motors assembly line. The team members serve only as technicians with precise directions, and as personalities they are scarcely distinguishable except by their different competences or functions.

The Plan always works. The IMF is as shrewd in anticipating the opposition's reactions to a certain stimulus as in organizing the available technologies; thus complications, one of the basic qualities of drama, are nonexistent here. In an age of technique, one can totally control circumstances to such an extent that the unexpected will not occur.

Moreover, the means by which the IMF traps its opponents reveals technique carried from the mechanical realm to the psychological. Not only does the IMF ruin the opponent's plans, but they do it by manipulating him into digging his own grave and at the last moment conveniently falling in. The operative plot dynamic is the assumption that if the proper technique is used, people can be forced to serve any purpose.

Admittedly, "Mission: Impossible" is among television's more preposterous fantasies, but only because the producers exaggerate its premises. Yet despite its fantasy, "Mission: Impossible" reflects aspects of our actual culture, aspects that Ellul has defined better than anyone else. The show's hero is not a man or even a group but technique itself, the ability to manipulate any situation totally, by means of the new mechanical, electronic, and psychological tools that we now have at our disposal. "Mission: Impossible" is not drama but process. It is not about people but machines, gadgets, techniques. It is a tribute not to the virtues of the human spirit but to the colder, more precise virtues of a thoroughly technical society. And this is the society that frightens Ellul.

Ellul's definition of technique is borrowed from Lasswell: technique is "the ensemble of practices by which one uses available resources in order to achieve certain valued ends." As he proceeds, however, this definition loses its focus. "Ensemble of practices" coalesces into the more rigid and organized conception of a distinct force that acts upon man in myriad subtle ways, a powerful environment with which men interact daily, yet because it is so omnipresent, so ironically obvious, they ignore it.

Ellul's reluctance to give analogies to technique or to suggest historical comparisons stems, no doubt, from his conviction that technique has a totally unique character. Yet the danger Ellul encounters resembles that of Teilhard de Chardin in his concept of the noosphere. If a phenomenon has no palpable existence, if one must resort to hyperbole in describing it; if it can be analyzed only in terms of its effects, then it verges on a precarious kind of mysticism. Ellul's erudition and convincing characterization of technique often distract the reader from this pitfall, but he leaves us finally with no explicit and satisfactory definition, and more of a glorified description.

If his definitions fail, however, he has other ways to help clarify the meaning of technique. He distinguishes, for example, between technique and machines. Although the machine is the best example of technique and its most symptomatic expression, it tends to be a source rather than the essence of technique. "Technique," he writes, "has enough of the mechanical in its nature to enable it to cope with the machine, but it surpasses and transcends the machine because it remains in close touch with the human order."

The conventional view of technology is that it constitutes applied science. Ellul disagrees. Yes, technique originally depended on science, but today, with the major laboratories staffed by technicians, with scientific advances requiring enormous outlays of equipment, with the scientific method itself being improved by technique, the roles have been reversed. "It is not the application which characterizes technique, for without technique, science has no way of existing." Science has become a handmaiden of technique; "pure science," claims Ellul, is a myth, as science has become only another means—a technique of its own.

As technique evolves, its field of activity moves from the mechanical and electronic to the social, economic, and administrative, and finally into the psychological. Ellul perceives in James Burnham's *The Managerial Revolution,* for example, the patterns of technique's recent stage of operation. The implicit effect of technique in social organization is standardization. "Standardization," Ellul quotes Antoine Mas, "means resolving *in advance* all the problems that might possibly impede the functioning of an organization." Mumford had stressed standardization in the products of technology, but had not considered it a distinctly *social* phenomenon. In Toynbee's work, organization appears as the hallmark of the period following the technical era. Ellul faults Toynbee for his inability to see the ultimate relationship between technique and organization; the sphere of influence has only broadened; the technical phenomenon, and thus the technical age, remains with us as never before.

Ellul's history of technique is uneven. Since he places most of the development of technique after the Industrial Revolution (Ellul calls it the "technical revolution"), his attempts at a prehistory tend to stem from obligation rather than insight. For example, in his comments on the function of magic in stimulating early technique, he lacks a sense of the profound connection that can be found in Mumford's *The Myth of the Machine*, in which magic helps educate man to the dimensions of his environment, and Malinowski's essay, "Magic, Science and Religion," in which magic is considered a scientific method in its own right, and an enormous step toward science and technology. Ellul makes one point that returns like a motif throughout his book: that magic, like technique after it, serves as a *safety barrier,* a guarantee against man's limitations in coping with the fearsome powers of the world around him. Though magic represents for Ellul the first expression of technique, its spiritual bias, providing only a peripheral grasp on materials and their uses, impeded evolutionary growth of technique. Magic is important not for where it leads but for what it reveals about man's need for technique.

Despite minor appearances of technique, particularly among

the Romans, Ellul characterizes the Greek, Roman, and early Christian periods as ages hostile to it. Only with the dawn of the industrial-technical revolution, where new techniques became apparent in the French armies, in the economics of the seventeenth-century physiocrats, and in the administrative procedures emerging after the French Revolution, does Ellul acknowledge a true growth of technique. A provincial French outlook must have led him to place the revolution that late, as Mumford has convincingly shown the influence of early mechanical clocks on medieval monasticism, and Lynn White, Jr., has argued similarly for the revolution in agrarian and social technologies that followed the introduction of the stirrup in the eleventh century. Fortunately Ellul's argument depends less on his historical interpretation than upon his conception of the character of technology, its contemporary and not its historical makeup.

Easily the two most convincing sections of *The Technological Society* are Chapter Two, "The Characterology of Technique," and Chapter Five, "Human Techniques." In each one Ellul describes technique as it operates observably within contemporary life, and the reader need not depend upon his involuted economic or political processes, which may or may not be quite as Ellul describes.

Is there anything new about the present aspect of technique? In asking this question, Ellul shows a reliance, implicit throughout the book, upon what has become known as Engels' Law: that in economics (for Ellul technical-social phenomena) changes in quantity can reach a threshold, creating a change of quality. The enormous massing of technique has, Ellul argues, "caused them literally to change their character." How then, can we observe their new character? By observing the characteristics of old and new techniques in their relation to society. Ellul is implicitly stating here that the true character of technique is invisible, apparent in its effects like an electron which is itself unseen but makes a visible path in a cloud chamber.

Techniques were employed in earlier times, says Ellul, within a larger structure and were modified considerably by those structures, but technical progress today is no longer affected by anything other than what Ellul calls its own "calculus of efficiency." A Danish woodworker and a French designer might approach the job of table-making with wholly distinct talents and conceptions. American and French aviation designers use the same procedures, the same mathematical factors, in designing a lightweight jet. Techniques have become thoroughly rational and separate from their cultural origins, virtually excluding spontaneity and personal creativity.

According to Ellul, contemporary technique has five characteristics, each of which supports and confirms the others: automatism, self-augmentation, monism, universalism, and autonomy. Ellul's discussion of these traits gives technique a clearer image than anything else he has written on it. They also support some of the darkest insights into Ellul's vision of society.

Automatism means the constriction of choices. In an area like medicine, new techniques invariably limit the number of options available to man. This may be, as in medicine, a considerable advantage, but Ellul sees it likewise as a negation of man's freedom. Indeed, as technicians dominate managerial and authoritative positions, and as technical problems become increasingly complex, the choices among methods and formulas become automatic; human intervention is not only unnecessary, but harmful.

Self-augmentation is closely allied with the final trait, autonomy. "At the present time," Ellul writes, "technique has arrived at such a point in its evolution that it is being transformed and is progressing, almost without decisive intervention by man." Growth is automatic, neither requiring nor giving way to human intervention. Moreover, the thrust seems not to be evolutionary as much as an almost inwardly controlled expansion. Ellul poses two laws of self-augmentation: that technical progress within a given civilization is irreversible, and that it proceeds geometrically, not arithmetically. He considers the automobile, the airplane, nuclear weaponry, and television as single examples of this principle. Ellul's concern does not lie with such individual phenomena, however, but with the whole network of interlocking techniques, which itself is moving at a faster pace than any of its subordinate factors.

"Monism" is a weak English equivalent of Ellul's *unicité;* the translator remarks that "holism" might have been a closer choice. The principle of monism suggests a much tighter unity than "ensemble of practices." Whether the techniques involved make possible the erection of a bridge, the promotion of a new hairspray, or a heart transplant, only their precise measurements differ, not their psychological force or their internal makeup. Instead of elucidating the structure common to them all, Ellul suggests that since technique has such a "monistic" form, it is foolish to try to differentiate between technique and its use. The common assumption that man can use or abuse his tools is only half true; as long as man follows the technical uses of his machines and techniques, he will be enabling them to follow their own distinctive lines of evolution.

A corollary to monism is what Ellul calls "the necessary linking together of techniques." No technique is an island. Techniques progress by interaction, interdependence, and an ever increasing expansion-reintegration action. A Lunar Apollo rocket can operate only through the integration of techniques as diverse and yet interdependent as radio engineering, fuel and thrust control, guidance systems, television, oxygen controls, computers, and a continued list that touches on most twentieth-century flight and communications technologies. Since they are always interacting, organizational techniques invariably transform economic and industrial techniques. Ellul concludes that "it is impossible to foresee all the consequences of a technical action."

Because it transcends cultural and ideological territories, technique is boundless or "universal," both geographically and qualitatively. Historically, commerce and war have spread new techniques throughout the world, but the more recent requirements for certain metals and industrial resources have speeded up the process considerably, creating in effect a network of techniques that encompasses the globe. All the quantities of a technological society, including technicians themselves, have become interchangeable between nations, creating a kind of technical noosphere, a world in which there is unity in nothing as much as the technical realm. The "qualitative" aspect of technique's universalism refers, ironically, to its use of a quantitative language and its own quantitative process. Thus the Japanese culture may be the seeding ground for an explosive new industrialization, but in the end Tokyo's Ginza strip resembles nothing so much as Times Square. Differences between civilizations mean nothing to technique, which operates on the same principles within all of them.

Whereas universalism seemingly offers hope for man (Buckminster Fuller's entire work is built on this premise), the final trait of technique, autonomy, is chilling. Mumford assumes that at every point in history man has controlled, or by negligence, chosen not to control, the growth of technology. Ellul counters this by claiming autonomy as the essential condition for the development of technique, as well as being one of its chief consequences. For a graphic example he refers to Kohn-Bramstedt's study of local police. For optimum efficiency, the police must be independent of political, economic, and even legal barriers. The most efficient police force will be found in a police state, where the technical organization has reached such autonomy that the complications of law or the deeper problem of justice have no foothold in police work.

Technique, governed only by its own autonomous impetus, accepts no judgment from without, nor any limitations. Politics, economics, morality, spiritual values, become immersed in its sphere, and not it in theirs. Ellul cites Giedion's study of the mechanization of bread production as an example of the confrontation between autonomous technique and the organic world. It is not a question of control, for technique can always guarantee better controls than man, who will forever be a source of unpredictability and potential error. Automated factories, a super-industrial economy, the unbridled weapons industry, for example, are everywhere.

Technique imposes its own ends upon all the processes it serves, but these are not as much ends in the human sense as further refractions of means: efficiency, speed, uniformity, even a destined obsolescence. Indeed, suggests Ellul, independently of whatever objectives man gives to any given technical means, that very means will always conceal in itself "a finality which cannot be evaded."

For Ellul, the old question, "Can man control his own technologies?" has no real meaning, as the autonomous character of technique denies man even such an option. It is, Ellul states flatly, all or nothing; once man has given technique its entree into society, there can be no curbing of its gathering influence, no possible way of forcing it to relinquish its power. Man can only witness and serve as the ironic beneficiary-victim of its power.

Heroes are men with destinies. While Ellul does not ascribe destiny to technique, he strongly implies that man, increasingly bounded by technique, has only the fragments of a destiny which belongs increasingly to society's new hero—technique.

THE TYRANNY OF TECHNIQUE

Technique wears a Janus face, and it is difficult at any time to be sure whether its newest phase is a boon or a disaster for man. All we can know is that finally, as its inroads invade even the most private and untechnical regions of society, its grasp becomes total. Ellul consistently emphasizes the totalitarian quality of technique. A corporation, already a visible emblem of technique, decides that for better harmony among its employees it will make psychological testing a precondition for employment. Suddenly men must answer multiple-choice questions (who, after all, assembles the testing data but the computer?) with information that previously belonged to the bedroom or the confessional. Eventually the same corporation might bring in group dynamics experts with their highly effective techniques to establish better rapport between employees. The final purpose behind all of this, of course, remains production. Efficiency, and not the lives of the men involved in production, is the goal that technique imposes and toward which it strives.

In a sense, *The Technological Society* is a gazeteer of the territories that technique has conquered and is presently conquering: the total sphere of economics, all of politics, leisure, sex, the gamut of human relationships, sport, religion, medicine, communications, and even finally, ecstasy. The range is not surprising. Throughout previous history technique belonged to a civilization and therefore remained only one factor within a larger cultural context. Today, however, technique "has taken over the whole of civilization." Man's most total environment is technique, and nothing he does, thinks, or feels can remain for long untouched by it.

In his interpretation of technique, Ellul shows far greater interest in effects than in causes. We see technique only dimly, in the traces it has made upon society, and working backwards toward an understanding of technique is like trying to interpret the path and velocity of a hurricane by viewing the wreckage it has made of a town. Indeed, Ellul suggests that the causal mechanisms may ultimately be beyond our scope anyway. Referring to the impact of technique upon economics, he says, "It is not the action of clear and certain causes which have produced this interdependence."

The method has its advantages, but its one crippling problem is proof. Although Ellul can clarify relationships, provide interpretations, and give visible form to a major cultural phenomenon, he cannot verify any of this with conclusive evidence. Perhaps, as he claims, and as Giedion, a remarkable historian himself, has postulated, the most important causes remain the most obscure. The effect, inevitably, is an approach to interpretation, particularly in economics and politics, which scales history to technique, and not technique to history.

Ellul's theory of the entrenchment of technique in economics takes a Marxist course. He is interested in the far-flung relationships between technical progress and development and the modern economy. He quotes Jean Marchal's statement: "The accumulation of machines transforms the economy," only Ellul substitutes technique for machines, stating that the transformation is thereby far more complete.

As technique develops, it spawns an interrelation between techniques as well as a thrust toward research and improvement. This forces a concentration of capital, soon leading to a corporation economy. In such an economy, state intervention or a managed economy is ultimately necessary, as the old safeguards such as Adam Smith's "invisible hand" no longer apply. Further, products become normalized, and the corporations discover that because of the pace of technical improvements, they must be marketed quickly, widely, and briefly. In effect, whether from the standpoint of the corporations or of the government, the economy becomes totally planned and controlled and subject less to the needs of people than to the managerial policies of the corporations and the power of advertising. Like all technique, economics becomes a totally planned and self-controlled phenomenon. Ellul considers planning as *the* technical method. In such an economic framework, and here Ellul departs significantly from Marx, it hardly matters whether the system is capitalist or socialist, because the process remains a function of technique, not of the economic system.

The same principle of technique overriding ideology applies in Ellul's discussion of the state. Here a central theme appears that he later extended to book length: the role of propaganda. As nationalism develops, Ellul claims, the heads of states depend increasingly upon technique, whether for waging war, for consolidating support, or for organizing different government functions such as the police, the legal system, the economy. Propaganda, though only one technique among many, tends to become such an important one that its role in further orienting society toward technique is as important as that of a planned economy. In either case, technique breeds technique, but in such a way as to conceal its significance as a major force.

The state's precise relationship to technique is complex and never fully defined. The state, meaning the controlling faculties of a society, shifts from its earlier political base to a technical base. Consequently, the enormous web of machinery and social and psychological methods available *to* a state in effect *become* the state. In such a political system, obviously, democracy is only an illusion, fabricated for the purpose of ensuring public apathy.

The totalitarian impetus of technique can adapt itself well to any political system, simply because its advantages—efficiency, organization, the guarantee of economic development

—are its only visible face. This was clear in Fascist Italy, Nazi Germany, and Stalinist Russia, but it is true even where political institutions have not been visibly altered. The threat posed by technique to the people in power is not apparent to them. Yet the takeover by technique, while it may even seem an improvement upon the politicians, contains its own particular danger, notably that man himself loses control over his environment and his destiny. Technique, once introduced into the state, has the consummate advantage of being able to organize and coordinate the total complex of the techniques that exist throughout society. From this point on, "man, practically speaking, no longer possesses any means of bringing action to bear upon technique." The state, which could have been man's ally, becomes instead alien to him. The smile of the Janus face becomes the leer of a spectre.

Nowhere, perhaps, are technique's infringements as profound as in the quality of personal, everyday life. While economics and the state both ensure a certain separation from man, "human techniques" exist to bridge all separations, finding new ways of appeasing man, smoothing out discordant feelings between men, extinguishing fragments of discontent. Here Ellul does not route his perceptions through intricate processions of economic or political theory, but presents his evidence directly and graphically. Two realms will be discussed here: the change in the physical, temporal, and intellectual environment, and the subsequent changes in man's identity. Technique has reshaped man's everyday environment, replacing the natural landscapes and contours with the hard, flat surfaces of the city. Space has undergone an "inverse revolution," contracting as population expands, so that isolation becomes the exception, and crowdedness the rule. Likewise, the visual horizons have changed. In another age, the natural horizon opened man to the world about him; today, "man knows only bounded horizons and reduced dimensions."

Daily work functions have been transformed by technique. Most workers today, including those in semi-automated factories, rarely come into contact with the materials and products on which they work. And as man's senses are extended by machines, his direct perceptual contact with the world he supposedly affects becomes less and less significant, and often less frequent. The technician in a laboratory may be working on a method for strengthening wood, and yet never feel its grain, never know it except through a microscope or spectrograph. Even the kitchen, with its age-old grip on natural foods, has become technicized, with its space tailored to functions (preparation, cooking, and washing), the motions of cooking systematized, and the ingredients increasingly pre-combined and packaged.

The clock, as Mumford recognized, is the primal machine of a technical culture, and Ellul attributes to it a growing control over the ways in which people live. Human rhythms are forced to adapt to the mechanical, essentially arbitrary, control of the clock. Besides determining when people will eat, sleep, awaken (decisions once based upon organic needs), the clock intrinsically quantifies man's experience of time. "Human life ceased to be an ensemble, a whole, and became a disconnected set of activities having no other bond than the fact that they were performed by the same individual."

Education has become the ward of technique, not only in the growth of technical subject matter, but in the elaboration of techniques for teaching and organizing the learning experience, even in nontechnical subjects. As educators increasingly move from knowledge skills to the child's personality development, the influence of the school, as well as the influence of technique, gains a firmer foothold in the educational process. Even though teachers themselves may be unaware of the process, children are being trained to adapt, trained to think technically, prepared for easy assimilation into the technicized society.

The leisure environment, ostensibly man's most hopeful escape from technique, has ironically become a further reinforcement of technique. The mechanical and electronic nature of the new forms of leisure—radio, television, movies—serve to intensify man's relationship to the machine, and through their reproduced images and sounds, further divorce man from his natural context. The escapist content of these media is a necessity for men today, claims Ellul, because their daily lives have been so stunted by technical controls that the earlier forms of leisure, such as conversations or games, have lost their meaning.

Ellul describes how, throughout all its previous encroachments upon man, technique alters the environment and thereby changes the shape and structures of human life. Some of Ellul's remarks go beyond this, however, to man's identity. Work in the technical society, he points out, assumes and implicitly creates a different type of man. Work today "implies in [man] an absence, whereas previously it implied a presence. This absence is active, critical, efficient; it engages the whole man and supposes that he is subordinated to its necessity and created for its ends."

Technique tends to restructure man's fundamental relationships, especially his relationship to a group. Ellul has repeatedly stated that technique is not a psychological or mystical phenomenon, but a sociological one. Like its tool, propaganda, it does not work upon man individually, but within a whole debilitating social context. And the process—adaptation—leads toward a situation in which man's identity is not "man-in-a-group," but man as an *element* of a group in which identity as such belongs to the group and man is only a component of it.

But Ellul's most ominous comments are to be found in his portrait of the technician, the archetypal man of the future. The technician occupies a mathematical universe; his choices can always be predetermined by arranging the factors he knows. Predictable, utterly dependent on technical know-how, he can be as creative or as imaginative as a technical problem demands. He has and lives by a scale of values, but these are values arising from technique: values of discipline, logic, consistency, efficiency, organization. These compose his morality, and he follows them righteously. Ellul admits that the process has only begun by which everyone in a technical society takes on this identity, but he sees the trend spreading rapidly.

Human techniques mean, in Ellul's world, human enslavement; they are the final grip of the technical environment that man cannot even fight, much less escape. Josef Goebbels once remarked: "You are at liberty to seek your salvation as you understand it, provided you do nothing to change the social order." This articulates, for Ellul, the "great law" of the technical society. Man has found a new god, new shrines, a new salvation; and in Ellul's dark prophecy the mistake is so grave he will never know the demonic scale of his delusion.

FROM INFORMATION TO PROPAGANDA

Propaganda: The Formation of Men's Attitudes, Ellul's follow-up to *The Technological Society,* expands many of the latter's ideas. It is a more trenchant and convincing sequel than *The Political Illusion,* which too often substitutes polemic for analysis.

A technical society, and especially its government, faces a unique dilemma. On the one hand, its powers have been concentrated by technology's tendency to organize and collectivize; on the other hand, that very technology has broken down old barriers between leaders and people. Men know more, and wish to know more; they also need to feel that they are participating in their leaders' decisions. These are only surface needs, however. Deeper and more urgent ones—for security, for belief in individuality and goodness—can be more influential in men's response to propaganda.

Propaganda, for Ellul, is an ineluctable adjunct to technique. He brings to it the same scrutiny and development, revealing a colossal phenomenon of untold significance. Whereas technique reduces the world to materials and numbers, propaganda reduces the world of the mind to clichés and near-truths. In both cases the process works by reduction, in a single, irreversible direction.

Most sociologists, particularly Americans, view propaganda implicitly as a psychological interaction between propagandist and propagandee. For Ellul this misses the total significance of propaganda as a sociological or environmental phenomenon, a cultural form that is larger than the sum of its parts. Most critically, Ellul differs with other sociologists in claiming that true propaganda need not be *intentionally* directed. On the contrary, it can be most potent, most thorough when there is no one consciously creating it. Propaganda is a process as much as a product, and the process, like technique, tends to become autonomous and self-perpetuating.

As with technique, Ellul never explicitly defines propaganda, but develops an elaborate description. He distinguishes between propaganda in the broad sense, including blatant forms such as advertising and political campaigning, as well as less evident forms, such as education, comic strips, and public relations, and propaganda in the narrow sense, which has an institutional character, such as virtually all the influences met by an army recruit in training camp.

For Ellul the critical questions about propaganda are not its techniques (indeed, here one can find one of his more notable weaknesses), but the interaction between propaganda and its social context. He discusses the forms of propaganda based on their social functions, its preconditions, its necessity, and its psychological and socio-political effects. Rather than writing an anatomy of propaganda, Ellul has approached the subject as an ecologist would study the introduction of a highway over a stretch of heretofore undisturbed terrain, showing how a drastic new influence enters an environment and slowly transforms it.

Ellul begins by expressing his familiar disdain for statistics and statistical methodologies. As a sociological phenomenon, he argues, propaganda cannot be faithfully analyzed on any level short of its total social dominance, and here the statistical methods prove worthless.

Ellul's distinctions often serve as the most valuable portions of *Propaganda.* He distinguishes between political and sociological propaganda. The former is the most familiar type, especially prominent in Communist nations; the latter receives less attention but is more effectual. "Basically it is the penetration of an ideology by means of its sociological context." This type of propaganda operates through diffusion rather than precise tactics; it does not result from deliberation and intention, but from the interaction of the media and a society. An American film shown abroad unwittingly promotes the American way of life and a certain level of material comfort. A television series contains assumptions about why men act as they do, what are the proper choices in certain circumstances, which values supersede others. As the communications media expand, the role of sociological propaganda likewise expands, leading toward a growing control of man's "information environment" which is the final aim of all propaganda.

Propaganda can be used to different effects: in one instance, to stir people into action; in another, to confirm ideas, impressions, or attitudes that they already possess. Ellul cites agitation and integration as the two critical goals of propagandists. Revolutions, insurrections, and reforms are the result of propaganda of agitation. It works to rouse people into changing their condition, usually through violence. The aim of integration propaganda is almost the precise opposite, to "stabilize the social body," to unify and reinforce it. Where agitation builds upon greviances and dissatisfaction, integration builds on comfort and contentment, even if these are sometimes illusory.

The sources of what Ellul calls "vertical" propaganda are leaders and authorities, men at the top who impose propaganda on those at the bottom. Goebbels's campagn in Nazi Germany is an excellent example. Vertical propaganda, the more traditional kind, "is in one sense the easiest to make, but its direct effects are extremely perishable, and it must be renewed constantly. It is primarily useful for agitation propaganda."

Horizontal propaganda is more recent, less evident. Instead of depending upon leaders to initiate it, it emerges totally from the group, as in the political propaganda of Mao Tse-tung's Chinese Communism, and the sociological propaganda of group dynamics in human relations. In both cases, the group itself initiates and provides the propaganda. In both, also, groups must not be in too much contact with other groups, and some educative process must be present. Schools are among the best examples of horizontal propaganda.

Ellul's final distinction between rational and irrational propaganda rests in the ostensible appeal of the former to facts, demonstrations, and rationality, and of the latter to passions and emotions. Although Ellul claims that irrational propaganda is disappearing, he admits that so-called rational propaganda often contains a number of distinctly emotional appeals, as in the case of television commercials.

"We do not talk to say something, but to obtain an effect," wrote Josef Goebbels. Propaganda is not simply the art of extricating desired effects, but the total framework by which information is presented and absorbed in today's society. The best propaganda is always the kind that comes closest to the truth, veering away only to the slight extent that the propagandist needs for his purpose. In Ellul's forecast, propaganda becomes increasingly necessary for society. But, as he states firmly, "Necessity never constitutes legitimacy." The obvious response to propaganda—education, new leadership, criticism of the media—can be no more than delusions, Ellul insists. Most probably they provide further guarantees of the vitality of propaganda in society. To fight propaganda with propaganda is to fight technique with technique. Man, as a free and spontaneous creature, can be only the victim.

A NEW MANICHAEISM?

Late in the third century a gnostic religion appeared that threatened the stability of early Christianity. Spread primarily by its prophet, Mani, it reached throughout the Mediterranean world, pushing as far west as Spain, as far east as China. The Manichaeans were persecuted by the Christians, but not before their doctrine had left is imprint on Christian theology.

The Manichaeans preached a radical dualism of good and evil, symbolized most graphically by spirit and matter. The Manichaean principle of evil was vitalistic, malevolent, active. Rather than Augustine's conception of evil as an absence, the Manichaeans envisioned evil searching out ways to tyrannize and malign man. The active force of evil was omnipresent and unavoidable. Only through knowledge and virtue could man find certain salvation. Any form of sacrament, any relationship beyond those set by the community, became infested by the evil that permeated man and his world.

In Ellul's moral universe, good and evil have taken on the guise of natural man versus technique. Not only are the two wholly irreconcilable, but it seems imperative, as it was with the Manichaeans, that one of the two must win the cosmic battle—and the clinches cannot go on forever. Ellul grants no middle ground. Most of man's attempt to extricate himself from techniques only involve new techniques, he says, and "technique can never engender freedom." Thus man must battle his enemy without the tempting weapons that his enemy holds before him, weapons that become increasingly popular among those committed to the war.

Ellul's genius is his greatest pitfall. In constructing the most comprehensive and far-reaching interpretation of technology to date, he has painted man into a corner, and given the world over to technique. His thesis is convincing, but so drastic as to refute common sense. And while he claims in several contexts that he is not pessimistic about the situation and that his spirit is not darkened by the prospects for man, he spends far more time pointing out the illusory character of proposed alternatives than proposing his own.

Is Ellul wholly deterministic? Must technique be interpreted only on the grand but seemingly fatalistic scale that Ellul gives it, or can his thesis somehow be salvaged from its exorbitant conclusions? These questions are critical, for Ellul's contribution to an understanding of the technical environment largely depends upon them.

Ellul does help clarify the precise nature of technique's determinism. In a paper titled "The Technological Order," presented to the Encyclopaedia Britannica Conference on the Technological Order in 1962, almost ten years after he wrote *The Technological Society,* Ellul used the phrase, "self-determining in a closed circle," a phrase harking back to Hegel. His only clarification of the phrase is his statement, "Like nature it [technique] is a closed organization which permits it to be self-determinative independently of all human invention." Its determinism therefore is of a relative rather than an absolute nature, but the main detrimental factor, human intervention, poses no threat in any way.

Technique's determinism has no final purpose. While technique is causal, Ellul claims, it is not directed to ends. Its own self-perpetuation and infectious reach to all aspects of society seems to be its final achievement, the accomplishment, like nature, of a self-sustaining process rather than a precise end.

What, then, of man? Is he or is he not free to challenge technique? How, exactly, does Ellul view man? Dimly. His sociology is built upon a premise, underlying all his major works, that "there is a collective sociological reality, which is independent of the individual." This reality, the distinctly collective character of men-in-society, is itself highly deterministic. "I do not maintain that the individual is more determined today than he has been in the past; rather, that he is differently determined." Ellul disclaims any treatment or the possibility of any treatment of the individual sphere. But eventually it becomes clear that many of the invasions of technique into privacy, leisure, work, education, even sex, take place not on Ellul's collective level, but with the individual.

Ellul has little patience with remedies proposed by sociologists, politicians, theologians, and especially scientists, which he regards as built upon a superficial analysis and therefore imposing some superficial solvent, usually new techniques. He repeatedly assails such proposals, insisting that "Technique, instead of provoking conflict, tends rather to *absorb* it, and to *integrate* instinctive and religious forces by giving them a plane within its structure." Thus to him, for example, Teilhard de Chardin represents Christianity given over to the wolves. Most solutions are as futile as the vision of the problem they purport to solve.

At this point, Ellul's vision of technique seems not only deterministic, but fatalistic as well. His own proposals, most clearly presented in his 1962 paper, purport to redeem his vision from its precarious fatalism. He poses five necessary conditions for a solution. Note that these do not comprise a solution; they are only the necessary preconditions before a solution can even become possible, so tightly, in Ellul's view, is man pinned down by the trap of technique.

The first of these is a correct diagnosis. This requires a general understanding of the heights and depths of technique, and a recognition that technology is far more than the sum total of its assembled units. The second condition, a pet Ellulian theme, is "the ruthless destruction of the 'myth' of technique, that is, the whole ideological construction and the tendency to consider technology as something possessing a sacred character." He applies this point especially to scientists and technicians. Third is the necessity to teach men a detachment and independence from technique—even, he suggests, humor toward it. This means, ultimately, choosing *not* to use certain techniques, choosing not to explore space, for example, or at least having the real (and not the illusory) freedom to make these choices. The fourth condition is the return of philosophy. "Authentic philosophy of real meaning would bring us precisely that possibility of mediation between man and the technical phenomenon without which any legitimate attitude is inconceivable." Finally, surely the most difficult point on the agenda, Ellul points to a dialogue between the "enlightened" (those who are aware of the problem) and the technicians. "Influencing technique necessarily means influencing the technicians."

Ellul's determinism is largely the result of his methodology, and any criticism of his thought must be directed here. Ellul's study comprises less a fixed doctrine than a reflective analysis, a study of society through its dependence on the mind-frame of technique. All Ellul's work has a nineteenth-century flavor, particularly when compared with the methods of, say, Fuller,

Innis, or McLuhan. His organization is architecturally sound, his elaborations endless, his logic impeccable, his categories complex and abstruse.

One of the most consistent features of Ellul's method is its dialectical structure. We learn technique largely through the ways in which it is like or contrary to nature. The interaction between technique and politics, technique and economics, technique and work, technique and human psychology, provides the real grist of Ellul's thought and the framework for its development. A notable, and perhaps necessary, consequence of this method is what translator John Wilkinson calls *The Technological Society*'s "histrionic irony." There is a kind of dramatic enticement here, as if Ellul were arguing with his unpersuaded alter ego throughout the book, shifting the point of view, oscillating from doubt to hope, from an unsettling fear to a hardy jeremiad.

Ellul's failure to illuminate the causal mechanisms of technique springs from his method, which can deal far more adequately with the present than with the past, a defect that is almost the exact opposite of Mumford's. In neglecting the historical, Ellul has suggested that what he describes as our present state is actually no more than a description of the process in which we are increasingly becoming involved. Indeed, in phrase after phrase he almost purposely leaves the tense uncertain, suggesting that we are becoming rather than that we already are presently the society that he describes. Further, his historical comments suggest that the movement of technique as such is cyclical, moving in from the material periphery of a society like a pendulum narrowing in on its own center, eventually reaching and absorbing man's most spiritual resources. If the implications never emerge into print, they nevertheless belong ultimately to his vision.

Ellul claims that we cannot really understand technique except in its relationship to other phenomena: economics, politics, work, leisure. The environment of technique is invisible, taking shape only in the world it transforms. Throughout Ellul's description the growth of technique is seen *mirrored,* but almost never seen through its causes. Man is clearly the victim of technique, but has he really caused his own downfall? Ellul never makes this plain. Ellul's final failure may well be that he gives man no real part in shaping the processes that threaten to destroy him. Man is depicted in the path of an oncoming bulldozer with no one in the driver's seat. And there is precious little in Ellul's work to suggest that there ever was.

Whereas Mumford and Giedion depict the influence of technology as a complex interaction between culture and technology, Ellul sees in the technological environments only one-way forces. Man, claims Ellul, can modify the world around him, and the world can change man. But these are two distinctly different processes with no discernible causal relationship. Moreover, the stronger of the two forces, technique, is so rooted in man and the world that he cannot truly fight it. You cannot confront technique, he says; it will only quietly absorb you.

Yet despite the overwhelming fatalism of Ellul's analysis, he has gone further than anyone else in characterizing and interpreting the dimensions of the technological phenomenon. He has found a principle by which the concept of technology can be taken beyond the machine and into social and psychological experience; an encounter group for Ellul is just as much of a technological phenomenon as a computer center.

Ellul has likewise, as Gerard Piel has noted, provided the first interpretation of technology that places the values *within* technology and not outside of it. The traditional ethic of the machine has always been that the machine is morally neutral; only man's use of it—his intentions, his control—determines its moral significance. Ellul argues persuasively that this is not the case at all. Technique contains its own values, and as technique is further assimilated into society these values of efficiency, organization, and precision become critical for the society at large.

Ellul's dark outlook undermines his genius but does not, in the final analysis, deny it. Despite its overwrought emphasis, *The Technological Society* remains a trenchant statement, the boldest yet to interpret the growth and significance of technology as a whole. Ellul may be a dismal prophet, but who can say with assurance that he is not largely an accurate one?

PART II

The Discovery of Media

SIX

Role-Playing of the Senses

> We can never be aware of the world as such, but only of . . . the impingements of physical forces on the sensory receptors.
>
> F. P. Kilpatrick,
> *Explorations in Transactional Psychology*

For Mumford, Giedion, and Ellul, technology is seen as a principle of change that reorganizes man's environment, shifts his institutions and behavioral patterns, and that almost necessarily dehumanizes him in some ways. Despite the hopes held out for technology, most notably by Mumford, the three men suggest that in the final count technology diminishes man; that its tendency toward greater wealth, better goods, speedier communications and transportation is finally more than offset by its reduction of man to its own terms.

Generally this viewpoint emerges from historical or sociological analysis, though to some extent it is rooted in a deep skepticism about the promises that technological utopians hold for society. But the viewpoint emerges likewise from a distinct concept of what comprises technology and the process of technological change. All three men concentrate on the development and cultural consequences of machinery: the industrial technologies of movable parts, separate, interrelated movements, and energy-transforming actions. Moreover, they consider the most important route by which new machines affect a culture to be the most observable one: the process of a new machine doing more work and thus creating for itself the economic guarantees that it will take over increasingly greater functions within the culture. This interpretation works as well for the present problem of automation as it did for the clock, the printing press, or the steam engine.

It could be said that the viewpoint these men espouse represents a nineteenth-century frame of reference. Mechanistic technologies were the cutting edge of new developments in the nineteenth century, and even though the gross national product of most industrialized countries may presently weigh in favor of mechanical technologies, it is clear that electronic technologies have become the forward thrust of the twentieth century: in the new developments they are catalyzing; in the forms of organization they create; in the way they are taking control of older, mechanized technologies (as in automated factories), and in the modes of thought they engender.

Mumford and Ellul make brief mention of electronic technology, but their major arguments build from the mechanical. Where they do include the electronic, it is usually within the pattern established by the mechanical. (Mumford includes the automobile in his assessment of the neotechnic phase, and considers the telegraph as a late paleotechnic device.) Technology for Mumford and Ellul is virtually identical with mechanization. (Giedion, perhaps conscious of this limitation, specifically focuses on mechanization processes in history.)

The difference between mechanical and electronic media can be seen most sharply in the purposes the technologies serve. From an ecological perspective, you can break down three types of technological environments: those that serve an ecology of goods (production facilities, factories, etc.); those that serve an ecology of man (transportation, architecture, etc.); and those that serve an ecology of information (communication media). The distinction applies most effectively to technologies of production and movement, such as the assembly line, the printing press, the automobile.

Within this perspective it becomes apparent that the major impact of most mechanized technologies was felt most critically in a shifting ecology of goods and people. The steamship and the locomotive speeded up the movement of merchandise and increased its availability—spurring further industry and the growth of cities. The airplane and the automobile permitted new kinds of mobility for men, enabling him to move faster, and creating, in turn, new communities and relationships between distant places.

To some extent the new electric technologies resemble the older, steam-based technologies. The telephone required a network of intersecting lines much as the railroad or steamships required their own networks. But the crucial difference in electronic technologies—and particularly the media—are twofold: a drastic new form of energy and a different purpose within most of the technologies—namely, information movement and control.

Electricity is mobile energy. Unlike steam, wind, or water power, it can be carried along wires to any distance. And while it has replaced older sources of energy—as in electrical trains—its most striking uses have not been merely as energy, but as the basis for new methods of communication and information control, such as the telegraph, the telephone, radio, television, and the computer.

The question posed by the electronic media is familiar enough: how "new" is the new? New enough, certainly, to suggest that any vital theory of environments would have to relate to these media on their own terms, and not in the vocabulary and constructs of nineteenth-century mechanisms. We know even less about an all-at-once ecology of information than we do of an ecology of man and goods after the steam engine. Electronic phenomena, which break through our old conceptions of space and time, have become the new (and as McLuhan emphasizes, invisible) environments against which past environments must be measured.

If the historians and theorists of mechanistic technology concentrated on the rhythms, breakdown of parts, and similar forces of the machine to suggest the process of environmental interaction, how can one approach the new electronic media —the circuitry of post-mechanized culture? The two major theorists of media are Harold Adams Innis and Marshall McLuhan. Both men, drawing on a rich but little-known wealth of data in historical, artistic, and perceptual studies, have disclosed a method as distinct from the nineteenth-century approach as are the conclusions they reach.

Mumford and Ellul conceived their work as *assessing the impact* of technological innovations. They concentrated on effects, and looked at the processes insofar as they clarified the effects. The ratio between man and his environment followed an easy formula: man creates a new environment; the unique features of its structure rebound back into man's life, affecting his institutions, personality, and ultimately (the moral dilemma) his alternatives for the future. The story of man-made environments is a story of effects, of man's inability to cope creatively with the rebounds.

For Innis and McLuhan such a ratio tends to obscure the real nature of man's relationship to his technologies. To begin with, they assume that the most important technologies are those that convey information. But these media must not be considered in terms of the information, or the content, they convey; rather, how each medium shapes and influences the information, and ultimately the culture. Innis and McLuhan have followed this question into a fascinating realm that opens up previously unthought-of dimensions for studying the nature of a new environment. For example, McLuhan interprets media as extensions of basic organic functions: a car is the foot, aided by an engine and wheels; a book extends the eye. The rebounding process here takes on an entirely fresh significance, since man is affected not by alien processes (mechanized time, interchangeable parts), but by his own organic extensions. Rather than polarize man and his environments as the previous theorists did, McLuhan suggests that a principle of organic continuity underlies all man's relationships to his technologies.

Normal historical reasoning cannot successfully follow the unique processes by which media are introduced into a culture and gradually change it. Whereas Mumford and Giedion looked for obvious effects and the processes that generated them, Innis and McLuhan have gone to the method of contemporary physicists—not attempting to follow a process whole, but to locate key junctures that reveal a pattern. Innis's writing, for example, seems unnecessarily dense: "Written codes not only implied uniformity, justice, and a belief in laws but also an element of rigidity and necessity for revolution and drastic change." But the density is a necessary consequence of his method: to show the interaction of media and various cultural institutions. Innis and McLuhan are less interested in effects than in what patterns a new medium makes when it jumps around, like an isotope in a cloud chamber, among the various agencies in the culture where it is introduced. Such a method makes for a different kind of observation, and, ultimately, for unique conclusions about the significance of new technologies. Yet as McLuhan has noted in his introduction to Innis's *Bias of Communications,* if one assumes that the medium modifies its content, then any valid study of media should move away from classification into pattern recognition.

The work of Innis and McLuhan, as well as the work of those who preceded them and contributed significantly to their own thought, reflect distinctly contemporary concerns. Culture is conceived as an information system; in other words, the interrelationships between events and institutions become more significant and more reliable evidence than the nature, stature, and organization of the things themselves. "You cannot know things," McLuhan has said, "you can only know the relationships between things."

Likewise, Innis and McLuhan have both shown a fresh skepticism about assumptions and conceptions. There is no environment we take for granted more than the media (whether language, telephone, books) that we use to discuss environments. As Innis has remarked, "The significance of a basic medium to its civilization is difficult to appraise since the means of appraisal are influenced by the media, and indeed the fact of appraisal appears to be peculiar to certain types of media." This very book is a form of written discourse, and reflects many of the biases that writing and printing have introduced into our culture: organization, the affectation of objectivity, the monologic structure. Innis and McLuhan have called attention to this problem, not only in what they have said about print, but in the curious, bewildering styles and structures of their books—dialogic, seemingly disorganized, yet taut with insight, indeed, using insight as the basic pattern for organizing data.

Mumford, Giedion, and Ellul defined environments to a large extent in terms of *force*. Each new phase represents for Mumford a fresh energy level, and Ellul describes technique as an invisible megaforce in modern society. The bias is understandable. The most obvious impact of technology historically is through the energy it has made available, and its ability to take on new kinds of work. Innis and McLuhan almost totally disregard force. As media, environments are defined largely through their major characteristics within a culture; for Innis, this means a temporal or a spatial bias; for Mc-

Luhan it means "hot" or "cool," individualizing or tribalizing. Environments may remain forces for Innis and McLuhan, but they do not speak of them that way. Indeed, throughout most of Innis's writing and much of McLuhan's, it becomes evident that environments are too vast, too invisible and elusive to submit to labels or categories. We cannot comprehend environments whole, but only aspects of them. It is an effort that demands probes and tentative relationships, not overarching theories.

The concentration on media as environments is only one aspect of the contribution made by Innis and McLuhan. McLuhan particularly has shown an interplay of sensory activity that gives the media a larger scope in history than Innis, with his emphasis on institutions and the time-space ratios of the media. Whereas Innis emphasizes how media transform the monopolies of knowledge and guarantee certain kinds of power within a culture, McLuhan goes further to suggest that a primary medium shapes the perceptual world of a people. Innis concentrates on media and power; McLuhan moves to a theme adapted only very late in Innis's work—the human sensorium.

In his first chapter of *The Presence of the Word,* Walter Ong, S. J., has shown the prevalence of an important problem in twentieth-century thought, what I call the "perceptual bias" question. The ranks of men who have grappled with the question look almost like footnotes from McLuhan's work verbatim: William Ivins, Karel Čapek, Adelbert Ames, Edward Hall, Siegfried Giedion, Rudolf Arnheim, E. H. Gombrich, Eric Havelock, and Walter Ong. The question cannot be isolated to any one discipline or the impact of any major thinker; some are art historians, others philosophers and physicists, psychologists and anthropologists. They have explored a range of problems emerging from a single question: How can a perceptual bias affect our awareness of what is outside us? The question has older origins in philosophers from Plato through Berkeley, in Bergson and Whitehead. Yet not until recently has it been given the social concern that these men bring to it.

The question of perceptual bias is the most important concern in the work of Marshall McLuhan. But as Ong has noted, the prevalence of these questions among people in so many different disciplines in recent years suggests that we have for the first time come to question the accuracy and unsuspected effects of our own perceptions. Buckminster Fuller has emphasized that at the frontiers of the sciences direct sensory data have been assumed by instruments with far more accuracy in seeing, hearing, touching. Never before in man's history has man become so conscious of the limitations of his unaided senses.

The problem of perceptual bias reflects a concern not only with perception and meaning; at its center is a fascination with the *relationship* between the two. Do we detect in a visual image a pattern that is already there, Gombrich asks, or do we impose upon it a pre-existing pattern already in our minds? The gestalt psychologists have posed the same question inside out, and come up with a totally different conclusion. Edward Hall has shown how our gestures and spatial relationships are really part of a complex language of which we are only partly aware—but a language that varies with cultures, creating difficulties in intercultural relationships. William Ivins has explored the relationship between the Greek bias for tactility and the motionless, isolated quality of Greek sculpture and the tactile qualities of Euclidean geometry. Throughout, these men have suggested that the workings of the human sensorium —previously thought to be as obvious as common sense dictated—may be one of the most complex and decisive factors in history.

Counterposed to the problem of perceptual bias is another,

less developed, question equally suspicious of previous assumptions. Benjamin Lee Whorf's well-known linguistic hypothesis is perhaps the best example of this area of inquiry—what I call the "media dictates culture" problem. Rather than call attention to sensory mechanisms, this question focuses on the media and particular ways in which the *medium* (and not a particular aspect of the sensorium) affects man. The work of Harold Innis centers on this problem, whereas McLuhan has attempted to encompass both.

Innis and McLuhan assume that a culture is defined by its movement of information, and that the conduits for that movement, or its "circuitry," deserve careful study. In an electronic age, these men are saying, we must think of environments afresh. We should look not simply to what is "out there," but also to the profound and unexpected processes between the "out there" and the "in here." Man does not relate to his environment like a ball being bounced against the walls of a closed room. He is constantly creating a new environment, and shaping it with biases that will mirror and thus redefine himself in many inexplicable ways.

ROLE-PLAYING OF THE SENSES

"Esse est percipe," wrote George Berkeley, one of the central figures of the Enlightenment. What is is what is perceived. Such an equation seems a great distance from McLuhan's equation two centuries later: "The medium is the message." Yet both follow a similar, if seemingly intricate and obtuse, logic. Both assume some tyranny of the senses. Both emphasize the difference in the qualities of perceptions between seeing, hearing, touching. Both show fascination with the all-important question: just how reliable is our sensory data, and to what extent is it determined by previous mindsets?

The significance of this question is illustrated by a fascinating experiment I once witnessed in a high school. Under the pretext of discussing how tastes differ, the teacher served all the students potato chips with a dip. Everyone tasted the dip, and different students suggested that it tasted sour, bitter, like onions, etc. Finally the teacher asked if anyone had tasted the rattlesnake meat: "the chunks in the dip." She produced the empty can and passed it around. Suddenly students were racing to the lavatories, clutching their mouths and stomachs. Why did they permit spoken words to upset the previous evidence of another of their senses?

The perceptual-meaning tradition can be traced back as far as Plato, whose allegory of the cave suggests that all we perceive is illusory anyway—vague shadows of the true realities, or Ideas. This led Plato to distrust sensory evidence, including extensions of the senses, such as writing. Aristotle later refined this idea by distinguishing between primary and secondary qualities. Primary qualities are those that last: the nature and biological continuance of trees, for example. Secondary qualities are those that change: the color of the leaves, a tree's height and texture—in effect, all our immediate sensory data about the tree.

Berkeley, emphasizing that all we have is our perceptions, said that Aristotle's distinction is facetious and Plato's allegory wrongheaded. *After* perception the mind may create its own categories and ideas, Berkeley suggested, but perception must always come first. Speaking of the sensory stimuli as "ideas," he wrote, "The ideas of Sense are allowed to have more reality in them, that is, to be more strong, orderly and coherent than the creatures of the mind." Berkeley's ideas led him to a quasi-denial of all reality when it is not being perceived; we inhabit a dream world given reality only by the use of our senses. His challenge to the normally accepted authority of uninspected sensory evidence shows that Berkeley anticipated one of the major problems faced by twentieth-century philosophers from Wittgenstein to Langer.

The tradition of thinkers dealing with the question of perception and perceptual bias in the twentieth century has a multitude of origins and directions. It is less an established "tradition" in the common sense of the word than a conglomerate of ideas relating to the problem of perceptual bias. Indeed, the occurrence of conflicting conclusions among these men is about as common as the instances in which they agree. Yet the fact that they are raising questions about the validity and significance of sensory experience means that they deserve some individual attention.

Excepting Innis and McLuhan, the perceptual bias theorists can be seen most strongly within two distinct fields: in experimental science—whether in studies of perception (Ames, Bekesy) or in the new anthropological science of "proxemics" (Edward Hall); and in art and architectural history (Gombrich, Kepes, Arnheim, Ivins, Giedion). These categories are partially valid, partially arbitrary. They are used here primarily to emphasize the major distinctions of these men within the context of a perceptual-meaning tradition.

The "transactional" school of psychology, named by F. P. Kilpatrick, defines a group of experimental scientists studying the nature and range of perceptual biases. "Transactional," Kilpatrick notes, refers to the basic assumption shared by these men: that man uses his senses not essentially to interpret his environment, but to interact with it. Using visually distorted figures such as slanted rooms, Adelbert Ames proved that to some extent we see what we want to see. The human eye tends to impose meaning (if simply in the form of structure) upon the phenomena that lie in front of it. F. P. Kilpatrick has pursued the forms of learning implicit in perceptual experience: to what extent we cling to the models that early perceptual learning consists of, and to what extent we change these models. William Ittleson's experiments in relative size as a cue to distance has resulted in conclusions similar to those of Ames: underlying sensory experience there is a familiar pattern of semiconscious data that the sense draw upon to interpret and structure what they perceive.

One book that more than any other has organized the findings of the transactional psychologists (as well as the work in other fields of perception) is James Gibson's *Perception of the Visual World.* Gibson distinguishes between the retinal image and the "visual world"—what is reflected on the retina of the eye, and what we consciously "see." Previous learning plays an enormous part in visual perception, Gibson argues, and the visual world is constructed as much by previous experiences and correlations (between size and distance, for example) as it is by the actual pattern of light, shadow, color, texture, and form that coalesces in the retina.

"There is a growing accumulation of evidence," writes anthropologist Edward T. Hall, "to indicate that man has no direct contact with experience per se but that there is an intervening set of patterns which channel his senses and his thoughts, causing him to react one way when someone else with different underlying patterns will react as *his* experience dictates." Hall has taken the conclusions of the transactional psychologists into the novel area of experimental anthropology. Hall's work with spatial dynamics, what he calls the new science of "proxemics," illustrates the critical role that space as a unique, if infra-conscious, language can play within a culture.

Hall's findings are among the most important in the perceptual bias tradition, as they mark more distinctly than most the latitude and significance of man's interaction with his environment. Though Hall concerns himself primarily with spatial dynamics and other forms of non-verbal communication, he places a great deal of emphasis on perception, particularly the dominant sense of a culture. "Man's relationship to his environment is a function of his sensory apparatus plus how this apparatus is conditioned to respond." Our senses and the way they work serve as the blueprint of a culture's communication system. Moreover, Hall defines environment largely as that system. The arrangement of furniture in a living room not only serves to involve the senses on a variety of levels; it likewise communicates—semi-consciously and unintentionally, perhaps, but communication all the same.

Hall's work emphasizes the differences between sensory relationships to the environment. The infant who reaches and grasps for everything inhabits tactile space; the musician who moves his instruments around on a stage to test the sound quality inhabits aural space. Our experience of space results largely from the bias of a culture. The French, trained to savor touches and smells, relate far more comfortably at close distances than Americans, who have been taught to resent most touching and who rarely associate within what Hall calls the "olfactory zone."

On one level Hall is pursuing a major tenet of McLuhan's thought: that sensory worlds, or sensory ratios, determine the quality and nature of a culture. On another level he explores the patterns of human ecology on a minute scale. His studies consistently reflect the wide range of spatial dynamics that play such an important role in all cultural exchanges, but of which we are almost totally unaware. "Most communications," Hall writes, "are in themselves abstractions of events that occur on multiple levels, many of which are not at first apparent." We are always encountering and expressing more than we know, and less than we are conscious of.

Edward Hall's fascination with spatial dynamics finds ready allies in the second field where the question of perceptual bias has been raised—among a number of recent historians of art and architecture. One of the most distinctive features of recent art history and criticism is the merging of art historian with psychologist. Rudolf Arnheim, a highly adept gestalt psychologist, is perhaps the best example of this trend; his *Art and Visual Perception* has become a classic in the perceptual substructures of art. Standing almost at a polar extreme is E. H. Gombrich, whose psychology is much more eclectic, and whose theories emphasize the bias that we bring to the perception of a work of art (or the bias an artist brings to its creation). György Kepes and Siegfried Giedion have both dealt with contemporary art and architecture with overtones of the Bauhaus mystique: how can art or architecture bring new unity to a fractured society? The work of William M. Ivins, Jr., for years curator of prints at the Metropolitan Museum of Art, stands uniquely alone: one of the closest anticipators of McLuhan, Ivins has shown better than anyone before McLuhan how extensive a single perceptual bias could be within a culture.

E. H. Gombrich's thesis, as set forth in *Art and Illusion,* does not lend itself to easy summary. In the 1890s a neoclassical sculptor and art theorist named Adolf von Hildebrand rebuked the naturalist painters by showing that the artist brings far more to a painting than simply what he sees. He knows from touch, for example, that a tree trunk is round, and not flat as it might appear from where he is sitting. Von Hildebrand's ideas influenced Heinrich Wölfflin, who emphasized "the history of seeing" and raised the question for twentieth-century historians: can a painter represent what he sees at any one moment with true fidelity to that perception? In effect, what is most influential—previous perceptions and mindsets, or the present perception?

Spanning a history of art that ranges from Giotto to Thurber, Gombrich argues for various interpretations of art and perception, all of which center around the original von

Hildebrand assertion that previous perceptual biases are more decisive in shaping and viewing a work of art than immediate perception. For example, Gombrich argues that the standard for a work of art is the degree to which it meets the perceptual needs and expectations of its period. He likewise states that caricatures (cartoon figures) can "work" only when the proper mental set is prepared to receive it.

Rudolf Arnheim has written what may be the best criticism of Gombrich's book, in an essay titled "Art History and Partial God." Arnheim's own work consists essentially in applying gestalt theory to problems of art interpretation and history. In approaching Gombrich he has shown that the over-emphasis on a previous perceptual bias (as against the perceptual guidelines suggested by gestalt psychologists, such as figure and ground) leads inevitably toward interpreting works of art as the reflections of earlier influences—in effect of stripping creativity and passion from art.

Two critical questions have dominated Arnheim's work: how gestalt psychology functions in the ways we relate to a work of art; and the possibilities of a peculiarly nonlinguistic, *visual* mode of thinking. Particularly in the second question Arnheim has contributed to a fresh understanding of the potential inherent in a perceptual bias. In his most pointed essay on visual thinking, "The Myth of the Bleating Lamb," Arnheim concludes that we need to learn to think in direct visual terms, without the impediment of language. Such a conclusion flies directly in the face of Bergson, Čapek, McLuhan, and others, who conclude that our thinking is already *too* visual—that the spatial bias of recent centuries has overwhelmed our ability to relate effectively to temporal and other nonspatial phenomena.

A chapter has already been devoted to Siegfried Giedion's work in the history of mechanization in the nineteenth century. To place Giedion within the framework of Mumford and

Ellul is only partly valid, as his other works, particularly *Space, Time and Architecture,* and the two impressive volumes in *The Eternal Present: The Beginnings of Art and Architecture,* reflects a concern with perceptual emphasis, especially in spatial configurations. Part VI of *The Beginnings of Art* is entitled, "The Space Conception of Prehistory." Here Giedion describes "acoustic space"—a term that would later become highly important for McLuhan. Eskimos and most primitive peoples regard space in terms of its emptiness, not what fills it (as visually biased civilizations do). "It may be," comments Giedion, "that the intangibility so prevalent in paleolithic art is a product of its relation to audible space. The figurations in the caverns appear and disappear from one moment to the next. Their aspect is dynamic, not static. Like sounds, they come and go."

Gombrich and Giedion both suggest the possibility of a perceptual bias on the cultural level. William Ivins suggests that every civilization is dominated by such a bias, and he was one of the first to explore exactly how it works. *Art and Geometry: A Study in Space Intuitions* is a remarkable little book, barely more than an extended essay, yet raising large questions that generations of previous historians had neglected. Ivins, perhaps more than anyone else mentioned here, was highly conscious of the fact that the deeper an assumption lies in a culture, the less likely anyone is to question or even consider it. Thus rather than attempt an analysis of the contemporary perceptual bias (what McLuhan has done, out of folly or genius), Ivins concentrates on the perceptual bias of the Greeks. Studying their art and architecture, he shows that tactility, rather than visual consciousness, guided, indeed dictated, their culture.

Greek sculpture and architecture illustrate well the tactile bias in Greek art. The statues at the Acropolis are separate objects with no interrelatedness. The forms reveal high craftsmanship, but seem the embodiments of some distant ideal rather than the imitations of living, vibrant human beings. The figures suggest no movement or tension, their stasis is permanent, eternal. It is as though they were constructed painstakingly by blind men, who could work with distinct forms, but were unable to convey any sense of perspective or large order.

The Greek tactile bias is everywhere in its architecture. Delphi, Olympia, and the Acropolis are built from the simplest (and most tactile) principle of building: pure compression. Moreover, as Ivins remarks about models of these cities, "The immediately noticeable things in these accurate models is that each monument, statue, theatre, temple, is placed wherever room can be found for it, like pots on an untidy shelf, with no thought of vistas or approaches, and no thought that any one erection could get in the way of or make any difference in another. . . . The only thing that can account for that is an obliviousness to an interrelated or organized visual order."

Euclidean geometry likewise reflects the tactile bias in Greek culture. All the theorems of Greek geometry exist independently, like unconnected spheres moving loosely through space. The world of touch is discontinuous and almost non-relational. The Greeks approached the spatial demands of geometry much as they approached the spatial demands of art: rejecting the visual space of sight, and choosing the space of the hand, where the eye's "empty space" becomes the choosing the "full space" as it is felt by the hand over the "empty space" as it is seen by the eye.

The Greeks' bias for tactility penetrated their logic, their philosophy, their poetry. Only after Alberti and the growth of perspective in Renaissance art did Western man totally overthrow this bias. Despite the significant contributions of other art historians like Arnheim, Giedion, and Gombrich, Ivins was the first to approach art primarily as *reflections* of a perceptual bias.

The work of these men—the transactional psychologists, Hall, Giedion, Gombrich, Ivins—represents a range of fields and different frames of reference. Yet all these men have recognized as a major problem the question of perception: to what extent is our perception of the world shaded, or even governed, by previous biases and mindsets? All these men reveal a wariness, a cautious suspicion toward perceptions and the conceptions that result from familiar perceptions. All of them imply that perceptions can somehow be biased, and that the problem of locating and understanding perceptual biases may be one of the central problems of our age.

DO MEDIA DICTATE CULTURE?

Culture, says Ellul, is propaganda in action. Ellul's study of propaganda suggests that every bombardment—every ad, every political statement, every interior decoration for a set on a TV series—is a form of propaganda. The media intensify propaganda by widening its ambits, and speeding up its action.

However, is this a complete conception of the media? Throughout his writings Ellul suggests that film, radio, and television simply conduct information, and the informaton serves as the propaganda. That conception—the familiar established idea of media—has been challenged by Innis and overthrown by McLuhan, who have both concentrated on the *forms* of media as the key to the ways in which they have reshaped cultures and personalities.

The idea, applied on Innis's historical scale and McLuhan's cosmic scale, is a new one. Plato was wary of permitting a written record to replace oral discourse, and philosophers from Locke to Wittgenstein have linked the structure of language to the structure of thought. But until Innis and McLuhan the idea that a *medium* shapes us more thoroughly than its content has received scarce attention. Suggestions in this direction can be found in the recent work of Walter Ong, S.J., and Eric Havelock. But perhaps nowhere else was the Innis-McLuhan theory of media anticipated as in the Sapir-Whorf hypothesis in linguistics.

Benjamin Lee Whorf came to linguistics from an earlier training in electrical engineering at M.I.T. His academic work, mostly under Edward Sapir at Princeton, came only during and after his years in the field studying the languages of the Mayas and the Hopi Indians. Despite the fact that only a trickle of his extensive writings were published during his lifetime (he died at the age of 43 in 1941) his theory of language, never more than hypothesis, has become one of the landmarks of contemporary linguistics.

No one has ever really "proved" the Whorf hypothesis, nor has anyone convincingly disproved it. Numerous attempts have been made both ways. It is a measure of Whorf's audacity and the revolutionary proportions of his work that the thesis cannot be proved or disproved, at least using present techniques. Whorf challenged two of the most beloved assumptions of our civilization: that there are no boundaries to thought, and that communication between two people of totally different cultures is ultimately possible. His work, like that of Freud, seemed to posit a new determinism, seemed to restrict man's freedom and therefore impale a precious image of himself.

There are essentially two tenets to the Whorfian hypothesis: that sophisticated thought requires language; and that the underlying structure of a language will totally control the way in which people are capable of thinking about the world. The first tenet contains nothing new. As Julian Huxley has commented, "The evolution of verbal concepts opened the door to all further achievements of man's thought." But the first tenet becomes exceptionally important when one looks carefully at the second.

When a Hopi Indian wants to say "He is running," he will use the word *"Wari." "Wari"* is also the Hopi equivalent of "He ran." There is no tense in Hopi. "What are to English differences of time," comments Whorf, "are to Hopi differences in the kind of validity." Such clues led Whorf to a careful study of the substructure of the Hopi language. The Hopis, for example, do not conceive of time as people using the Western languages do. There are no words to describe yesterday or tomorrow, or to provide categories of time, such as hours, days, weeks. Nor are the categories between space and time decisive in Hopi as they are in English. As Stuart Chase has commented, the Hopis are linguistically much closer to understanding relativity and quantum physics than the English-speaking peoples.

For Whorf, such biases that undergird a language not only reflect the cultural needs and character of the people, but likewise serve to limit and constrict the kinds of thought possible within the language. No Hopi could have written an accurate equivalent of Shakespeare's *Coriolanus,* which reflects a distinctly Western conception of time. Not only are languages relative, but so are the world-views that they control. Whorf calls it the principle of linguistic relativity. "We are thus introduced to a new principle of relativity, which holds that all observers are not led by the same physical evidence to the same picture of the universe, unless their linguistic backgrounds are similar, or can in some way be calibrated."

Whorf's hypothesis marks the first major step toward a field theory of media as forms. Language cannot be understood adequately as a technology, an environment, and a medium, unless its total relation to the culture becomes the focus for study. Whorf's work, while tentative and far from being a whole system, concentrates on relationships, locating language within its cultural context and analyzing it in terms of its dynamic interplay with the culture.

A historian who has dealt with another aspect of this problem of media is Walter Ong, S.J. Ong's *Ramus: Method and the Decay of Dialogue* shows the reaction to the printing press in the sixteenth century as reflected in Peter Ramus, a popular writer of the time. Ong concentrates particularly on the shifts from oral modes of discourse and dialogue to the new properties of the written word. "For at the heart of the Ramist enterprise is the drive to tie down words themselves, rather than other representations, in simple geometrical patterns. Words are believed to be recalcitrant insofar as they derive from a world of sound, voices, cries; the Ramist ambition is to neutralize this connection by processing what is of itself nonspatial in order to reduce it to space in the starkest way possible. . . . Printed or written words themselves must be deployed in spatial relationships, and the resulting schemata thought of as a key to their meanings."

In a later book, *The Presence of the Word,* Ong has pursued the same theme toward the distinctive character of oral-aural expression. *The Presence of the Word* is one of the most important books to follow in the wake of McLuhan's *Gutenberg Galaxy* and *Understanding Media.* Ong accepts the Innis-McLuhan assumption that since the printing press the Western world has been dominated by its visual bias, and he pursues the question of what values would distinguish a return to an aurally based society. He uses McLuhan's three major periods of media—pre-alphabetic aural (what McLuhan refers to as "tribal"), alphabetic and later typographic, and electronic. In one fascinating chapter he parallels these periods with the three stages of development in Freud: the oral stage (assimilation), the anal stage (constriction), the genital stage (orgasm).

While Ong admits the limitations of these comparisons, such exploration reflects a lively and much-needed approach to media.

Like McLuhan, Ong considers the senses the proper route to understanding media and their effects on the human sensorium. "What we are faced by today is a sensorium not merely extended by the various media but also so reflected and refracted inside and outside itself in so many directions as to be thus far utterly bewildering. Our situation is one of more and more complex interactions." Ong speaks not only for himself, but for an increasingly growing group of thinkers for whom our perceptions are more important than what they purport to perceive.

TOWARD A PRINCIPLE OF ORGANIC CONTINUITY

In counterposing man to his environment, Mumford, Giedion, and Ellul (as well as generations of social scientists and historians) have shown that the breakdown of the old ecology leads to imminent disaster for man and his world. This may be true enough—of the old environment. Yet even as electricity supplants the steam engine and the motion picture becomes late-night television, a new environment emerges—and one that seems to demand fresh conceptualization of what an environment is and how it interacts with man.

By exploring the relationship between perception and meaning and the power of media within their cultures, the men briefly mentioned in this chapter have prepared the way for a conception of environment built not on its influence on man, but on an organic continuity with him. Electricity, McLuhan observes, is an extension of the central nervous system. McLuhan, drawing upon the people described in this chapter and particularly Harold Innis, has conceived the technological environment afresh in terms of its most vital relationship to man, not simply in terms of its differences from him. Culture flows in an unbroken circuit between man and his environment. The old ideas of technology and culture, the two-cultures polarizations, the argument that technology has killed art, shatter like so many carefully preserved keepsakes out of the past. Technology changes culture, yes, but not by grossly defacing it. A new technology rearranges our perceptual world, and subtly redefines our relationship to our environment.

The men who have explored perceptual biases and the importance of media all reveal an illuminating common feature: a restraint from making (or worse, imposing) value judgments. Bertrand Russell has said that the major discovery of the twentieth century was the suspended judgment. A good theory can be part evidence, part guesswork. But the important thing is to recognize that a theory *can* be valid, even if we don't know for sure. In an uncertain age value judgments can be as much of an impediment as horses lined up to pull a car. Ames, Hall, Gombrich, Giedion, Arnheim, Ivins, Whorf, Ong, and the others have dealt with questions that certainly lead to important questions of value. But they have been wise enough to avoid the pronouncements, at once so perilous and unnecessary. What we need to know most is not how bad things are, or how good things are, but just how things are.

Another important feature of the man described here is the diversity of method. A significant point is that many of them created their best work outside the field for which they were trained: Rudolf Arnheim came to art from gestalt psychology; Gombrich came to psychology from art history; Ong is an assiduous scholar in sixteenth-century studies; Whorf trained at M.I.T. as an electrical engineer. Innis was an economist, McLuhan a professor of English. These men have shown that specialized fields should be giving way to habits of thought that can transcend a single discipline. In an age of electrical circuitry, the mechanical segmentation of ideas can be as absurd as running power lines into gas lamps.

"All real scientists," Benjamin Lee Whorf has written, "have their eyes primarily on background phenomena in our daily lives; and yet our studies have a way of bringing out a close relation between these unsuspecting realms . . . and . . . foreground activities." The problem of new technologies and the impact they exert upon a culture is certainly a "background phenomenon." Yet as we become more cognizant of this problem and its importance, the larger questions of the nature of technology and its implications for society become increasingly critical. Beginning with a principle of disparity between man and technology, Mumford, Giedion, and particularly Ellul have explored the problem and reached their conclusions. Innis and more notably McLuhan begin with a principle of organic continuity between man and his technologies; their explorations do not mark so much a negation of the earlier tradition, but a fresh and original beginning.

SEVEN

The Routes of Minerva's Owl

HAROLD ADAMS INNIS

> We can perhaps assume that the use of a medium of communication over a long period will to some extent determine the character of knowledge to be communicated and suggest that its pervasive influence will eventually create a civilization in which life and flexibility will become exceedingly difficult to maintain and that the advantages of a new medium will become such as to lead to the emergence of a new culture.
>
> H. A. Innis, *The Bias of Communications*

Fully armed and full-grown, Minerva sprang from the head of Zeus to become one of his most trusted goddesses. She was the protector of the city and its activities: the professions, the arts and crafts. As was common among many of the Roman goddesses, she was preceded in her movement by her owl. H. A. Innis opens his most important essay by quoting Hegel: "Minerva's owl begins its flight only in the gathering dusk. . . ."

The idea is hardly a new one, that a culture begins its disintegration with its highest and most creative period; Toynbee thought so, and Hegel considered it a necessary phase of decline and revitalization. Innis follows the flight of Minerva's owl into new quarters, however, suggesting that the process of cultural growth and expansion flows not from genius or empire but from media. Minerva's owl follows the route of a new form of communication—whether it be script, oral tradition, or print. Minerva, in Innis's thought, becomes the greatest of muses, and her owl the clue to the mysterious ways in which she works.

Harold Innis is best known as one of the major figures in Canadian economic history; the London *Times Literary Supplement* has called him "Canada's first and perhaps only genuine intellectual." Born in Ontario in 1894, Innis studied at McMaster University and later at the University of Chicago. He received his Ph.D. at Chicago shortly after World War I, when the new social thought of Thorstein Veblen, George Herbert Mead, and Robert Ezra Park reached its most vital period there. Veblen's evolutionary theory of economic development, Mead's focus on language, and Park's concern with control mechanisms in culture undergird Innis's thought, especially his later work in history as a refraction of its communication forms.

Innis's early writings belong to two phases: his economic histories, such as *The Fur Trade in Canada, The Cod Fisheries, Essays in Canadian Economic History;* and his "media bias" phase, which includes most of his writings from the late 1940s to his death in 1952: *Empire and Communications,* and his single most important work, *The Bias of Communication.* The two phases are separated less by method than by focus. Innis's approach to economic history was to follow the patterns created by the movements and uses of economic staples such as fur, wheat, and timber, and to study economic changes through these patterns. Thus at the turn of the century the rise of the newspapers created a growing demand for wood pulp. This had profound effects on both the lumber industry and the Canadian economy. In his later work Innis concentrated on the precise mechanics in the growth of the newspapers; the fresh focus gave him a fresh, and startlingly original, vantage point for recognizing the unique role of a new medium in shaping an economy and new social institutions. Innis the economic historian became Innis the cultural historian, and by the profound implications of his conclusions, Innis the philosopher.

Innis's work in economic history confronted him with several critical questions that dominate his later writings. What is the source and route of new forms of power and authority? How do changes in *forms* (particularly forms of communication) affect social institutions and the quality of culture? Finally, how can a culture maintain stability and its highest period of creative activity? Economic history could only provide Innis with the skeleton of a society; he wanted to see where the veins carried the blood.

For Innis the most critical factor in a society is its communications. Not so much *what* is communicated, but how specific communications media operate, what presuppositions they impart to the culture, what forms of power they create. The key to cultural change is the predominant communication medium in a culture. Innis defines media broadly: they include spoken language, the materials for writing (such as papyrus and scroll, stylus and reed), the structure of the written word (as hieroglyphs or alphabet), print and electronic transmission. For Innis, the medium is the critical factor that reshapes cultures whole.

Two categories explain the influence of communications medium: space and time. The use of clay tablets in Babylon confined information to a limited space, but guaranteed its durability. Papyrus, on the other hand, was available in great quantity for the Romans; it was light, easy to transport, and enabled information to move to the far-flung corners of the empire. Consequently, as Innis explains it, Babylon was a culture with a sturdy temporal bias; Rome had a spatial bias.

The "bias of communication" is, therefore, the temporal or spatial tendency that will determine the orientation of a culture. Innis describes this process as the "monopoly of knowledge." A new medium favors a fresh flow of information; inevitably, a small group (favored by the nature of the bias) will move within that flow and take power. In a spatially oriented society, this group tends to be secular, centralized, and imperialistic. In a temporally oriented society, this group will be religious, conservative, legalistic.

Innis follows history much as a high-speed camera might follow the endless ricochets of a bullet within a confined chamber. His dynamics are almost Hegelian in their elaborate dialectic between the spatial bias and the temporal bias. For Innis, history is a succession of subversions. Once a spatial bias has established power, as in imperial Rome, that power becomes immediately susceptible to the rise of a new power, such as the oral Christians, whose Church undermined and eventually inherited the legacy of Rome.

There is a moral concern implicit in Innis, not shrill and overbearing as in Spengler, or structurally dominant as in Toynbee, but surely more noticeable than the moral vein in McLuhan. Innis wants not only to chart the course of Minerva's owl, but to learn *why* it alights where it does. In the Golden Age of Greece, the high period of Byzantium, or the Renaissance, culture flowered and reached a precarious, but nonetheless precious, stability. Why? Innis argues it is because the cultural bias of each period is met with consciousness of the opposite bias. Time and space achieve that rare equilibrium that keeps a magnet balanced in air or the seesaw from tipping either way. Indeed, the very continuation of a culture depends primarily upon the ability to strike a balance between temporal and spatial tendencies. In *Empire and Communications,* Innis writes, "Large scale political organizations such as empires must be considered from the standpoint of two dimensions, those of space and time, and persist by overcoming the bias of media which over-emphasize either dimension."

Heinrich von Eicken has asserted that the master key to

history lies in human actions provoking violent reactions: in the swing of that pendulum is felt all the force of human time. Innis essentially agrees with that theory, though he adds that new media are the initiators of fresh reactions. Innis has attempted reading history through forms rather than content, through information flow and control rather than political heroes, wars, and trade. He is often closer in his thought to the cybernetic interpretation of Norbert Wiener (whom he probably never read) than to the awesome tradition of historians and philosophers from whom he draws such an array of data.

To look carefully at Innis's historical method, one might conclude almost immediately that it is a unique kind of madness. Innis cares little for chronology, and in one page might drift between the Counter-Reformation, the Babylonian dynasties, and Roman law. Yet he is writing history, not a field theory of history (at least in the sense that the theory is larger than the sum of its parts: with Innis, the "parts" often seem more important than their sum). The problem is an environmental one. Innis frames time. He will not bow to it, ignore it, place history within *its* context; rather, he places time within history. As long as a historian does not conceive of time as an environment, with its own distinct modalities and shaping influences in different cultures, that very environment is likely to escape his notice. Yet it controls and limits what he writes. Innis is concerned with the meaning of time for a particular civilization, including economic, linguistic, and geographical factors.

The framework for Innis's history, therefore, is not chronological, but environmental. Innis uses the introduction of new media as his focal points, and the modalities of time and space as his lines of stress. McLuhan describes the method succinctly. "Innis had hit upon the means of using history as the physicist uses the cloud chamber. By bouncing the unknown form against known forms, he discovered the nature of the new or little known form." History for Innis is spontaneous, discontinuous, depending more upon energetics than fixed institutions or dates. Innis has written the first post-Einsteinian history of civilization.

Innis is careful to emphasize that his method involves new trajectories, new pathways of historical causes, and that therefore he has not produced an all-embracing reconstruction of history, but a field theory, aided and animated by what McLuhan would later call "probes." He describes the essays in *The Bias of Communication* as working data arranged toward a conclusion; "They do not answer the question but are reflections stimulated by a consideration of it."

In contrast with McLuhan, or for that matter, other major historians such as Mumford, Toynbee, or Spengler, Innis rarely makes definitive generalized statements. He clings to his data, flinging it into new and often incomprehensible relationships; and usually he leaves the work of generalization to the reader. This is the monumental difficulty of Innis's writings; his prose is so intricate, his data so dense and unexpected, his conclusions so brisk, sudden, and yet often so momentous, that the reader feels overrun by Innis's erudition and originality and pace.

There are several reasons why Innis overpowers his reader; all of them can be traced to what might be called his "quantum logic." Innis has no patience or need for the slow steps in following a historical cause to its effects. Sentences convey the weight of tomes, and almost inevitably force careful, ponderous readings. In speaking of the medieval influence of paper, for example, he states: "Writing developed beyond monastic walls and in the twelfth century numerous attacks were made on ecclesiastical corruption." Or on the failure of the Counter-Reformation: "The military genius of Cromwell and of Gustavus Adolphus in using new instruments of warfare guaranteed the position of Protestantism in England and Germany." Innis prefers the quantum jump to the slow explication of interacting events. But it is a mighty demand to make upon the reader, and forces him into accepting a wealth of unstated assumptions simply to follow Innis's bolting lines of thought.

The second difficulty lies in Innis's use of resources. McLuhan has remarked that anyone who has checked out Innis's reference material "will be struck by the skill with which he has extracted exciting facts from dull expositions. He explored his source material with a 'geiger counter,' as it were." The quantum logic applies not only to Innis's writings but to the phenomenal number of quotations and references he gathers on every page. An example: "The equation of ethical values between cultures is possibly more difficult than the equation of other values, though Professor V. Gordon Childe has described the implications of cultural change in such fields of abstraction as mathematics. The outburst of rich artistic activity in Greece coincided with a decline in the status of women. Dean Inge has reminded us that the extreme sensitivity of modern civilization, for example in the attitude toward cruelty to animals, and the extreme insensitivity toward unbelievable cruelty to human beings have synchronized with the complete collapse of spontaneous and unconscious artistic production."

Innis's "quantum logic" is not only operative in his sentences and his use of references; the very construction of his writing, from sentence to sentence, from paragraph to paragraph, assumes that the reader can travel at his darting, sometimes reckless, speed. No doubt some can; McLuhan's own style, especially in *The Gutenberg Galaxy,* reveals as much of a dependence upon Innis's method as upon his ideas. Yet for most readers the impact of reading a few pages of Innis is the same as having used a super speed-reading technique on all the history shelves of a public library.

CULTURE'S SEESAW: TIME AND SPACE

Media, whether parchment, papyrus, or printing, create the pathways of information in a culture. By controlling the movement of communication, they determine a culture's "ecology of information"—the unique and dynamic relationship between a people and the knowledge available to them. Thus parchment, after the collapse of Rome, gave impetus to the rise of monasteries. Unlike papyrus, parchment preserves well, and is suitable for libraries and reference. But due to the exorbitant demands of scripting, the parchment books required organizations—monasteries—that could collect, preserve, and reproduce the books. Innis depicts the power hegemony of the monasteries in the Middle Ages as a consequence largely of the media of parchment and script.

Three essential factors control cultural growth and change within Innis's thought: media; the process whereby a new medium creates a temporal or spatial bias; and the far-ranging effects of this bias in the culture. Each of these factors deserves a careful analysis for a full comprehension of Innis's thought.

Innis does not distinguish between media except through the biases that they project. This is not to say that oral tradition is the same for Innis as stone, clay, or parchment, but only that the best insights Innis gives show the features that these media have in common, notably how they give cultures a temporal bias. Strictly speaking, Innis is not concerned with media. He concentrates rather on the temporal and spatial ramifications of certain media, looking to the media simply for clues to the larger patterns.

Media are rarely found alone in Innis's history. Almost always they exist in conjunction: clay and stylus, parchment and pen, paper and printing. Indeed, each conjunction determines the visual structure of the language itself—a medium all its own. Innis notes how the use of clay tablets in Mesopotamia introduced cuneiform writing, whereas the Egyptians, with access to quantities of papyrus, developed a pictograph system of writing. Clay, sparse and heavy, encouraged a frugal and compact system of writing, papyrus enabled an elaborate system. Our present alphabet may have originated in Babylonia, but the Greeks, with their strong oral tradition, were capable of transforming it into the flexible tool that has made a specifically *written* tradition possible.

Innis makes no attempt to categorize or neaten the tangled account of media in history, but he discerns seven rough stages. The first was the use of clay, the reed stylus, and cuneiform script originating in Mesopotamia at the dawn of civilization. These imposed a strong temporal bias—which can be seen in the religious strength of Egypt or the pyramids. The second stage began with the oral tradition in Greece allying itself with the written tradition after Plato; papyrus and brush (later the pen) combined with the alphabet to provide a light, spatially oriented system of communication. This dominated the West until the disruption of the Roman empire. The third stage was heralded by the orally conscious Church, but partly as a result of parchment and pen, the Church withdrew into the monasteries, where a temporal bias gave the Church its authority in the Middle Ages. After the twelfth century, paper and pen made the written word available on a large scale. The vernacular undermined the power of the Church and began the emergence of the spatial bias that would, after printing, give rise to nationalism, new modes of law and politics, and the dissolution of the Church. The fifth period began with the introduction of the printing press and movable type in the West. The spatial bias already begun by the vernacular grew steadily, transforming every institution in the West and leading inexorably toward a succession of violent revolutions and the growth of mechanized industry. Paper production and printing both became mechanized in the sixth period, further stretching the boundaries of written language, and enabling the sudden expansion of newspapers. Innis mentions, but gives little attention to, the seventh period: the cinema and radio, (and TV).

Such a historical account defines civilizations through their predominant media. Innis assumes not only that knowledge is the key to power, but the substructure of a civilization. And since each medium gives the knowledge it conveys a certain character, that character will define a civilization and help explain its development as well as its collapse.

Throughout his writings, Innis seems to emphasize three generic classes of media: oral language, written language, and printed language. These subsume the more specific forms such as hieroglyphs, parchment and pen, nonmechanized printing. Oral language, almost by definition, favors a bias of time. Written language can favor either space or time, depending upon the materials used. Printing, far more than any medium that preceded it, favors space.

Innis views oral communication as elemental to any civilization, but only at a few junctures in history as the primal source of communication. The early Greeks lived within an oral culture—a major reason, according to Innis, for their phenomenal cultural vitality. The oral word carries a force of its own; its authority need not arise from any social structure; and, as Innis shows by drawing upon Graham Wallas, an oral tradition provides an important basis for creative thought. Oral transmission emphasizes memory and training. The principal difficulty of the spoken word is its evanescence; no sooner is it uttered than it has disappeared forever. This limitation forces an oral culture to conserve its best information and guard it tightly against the ravages of forgetfulness and change. According to Innis social institutions in an oral culture tend to be relatively small and localized; the Greek city-states could be no larger than they were because of the inability to transmit ideas beyond the boundaries of a relatively contained communications system.

It is not an uncommon historical claim that written language was the basis for the growth of cities and early civilizations in the Tigris and Euphrates, Egypt, and Assyria. Innis neither bothers to agree with or challenge the claim, only to suggest that the character of each early civilization was shaped by the *form of writing* used.

Writing gave man a separate transpersonal memory. It broadened his ability for abstract thinking (thus enabling the development of mathematics and new sciences); it provided a new justification for authority and tended to concentrate power as never before. "The monarchies of Egypt and Persia, the Roman empire, and the city-states were essentially products of writing."

Writing, Innis states, "made possible the expression of fine distinctions and light shades of meaning." Whereas oral language had always conveyed feeling as well as meaning, written language moved away from feeling, in one sense freeing the process of thought, in another sense limiting it. Communication became more explicit, and thus an increasingly powerful tool in authority, economics, and law. McLuhan interprets the birth of writing as the beginning of a sensory shift from the ear to the eye. Innis chooses a more modest conclusion. Writing did not transform all society, but shifted the focus of power within various institutions. The exact nature of this shift within a particular culture would, he emphasized, depend upon the instruments and materials used for writing. Clay and parchment favored time and conservation; papyrus and paper encouraged empire.

Printing not only widens the ambits of the written word, it can produce many copies of the same sheet, newspaper, or book. The monopoly of knowledge possible when the monasteries controlled all the manuscripts collapsed in the wake of the printing press. The printing press dissolves geographical barriers, undermines the authority of the written word, makes opinion more important and more difficult to control. Innis quotes Thomas Jefferson: "The printers can never leave us in a state of perfect rest and union of opinion."

Before the printing press, most manuscripts and written words remained in the custody of the Church. Only a small percentage of the population could read, and at any rate most of the important books, including the Bible, were available only in Latin. The printing press democratized knowledge. The printing press not only enabled people to read more; it fostered habits of reading; it gave rise to more and larger universities, where the textbook displaced the lecture as the central source of information. The printing press gave new shape to knowledge and its uses.

Moreover, as Innis states, "the discovery of printing in the middle of the fifteenth century implied the beginning of a return to a type of civilization dominated by the eye rather than the ear." Printing has come to dominate society to such an extent, Innis suggests, that we can barely begin to comprehend the environment that it has created. Nationalism, individualism, the appearance of Luther and Calvin, the rise of a capitalist economy, specialization, industrialization, the corrosion of the Church's authority: these all belong to a historical process initiated by print. Innis shows how "freedom of the press," valued as a bulwark of our society, is actually one of the strongest mechanisms of the print bias for guaranteeing its continuity.

Eventually the mechanization of print gave added force to the revolution begun by Gutenberg. As new milling and pulping techniques produced more paper, the written word became increasingly less prestigious, less authoritative. Innis quotes a letter written early in the nineteenth century by Thomas Constable to a friend: "If you wish to become a great author your chance will be bye and bye when paper gets cheaper." Eventually mechanization of printing and paper production led to the mass-produced newspapers at the turn of the twentieth century. Innis only hints at the effects of mechanization upon communications; in regard to the newspapers he says that the new methods "divided reason and emotion and emphasized the latter."

Media operate invisibly. Innis considers them the most important environments within a culture, but as they contain the very movement of information so critical for the life of a culture, they rarely receive the attention they deserve. Since his own method avoids showing specifically *how* a medium effects changes in a culture, yet since that very question is so central to his argument, it is important that we undertake to trace the process ourselves.

Innis views any culture as an organism, struggling for equilibrium within a complex of tensions. The skeleton of this organism is the interactive structure of its institutions: politics, religion, law, economics. But its lifeblood, which essentially concerns Innis, is its movement of information. Culture, he writes, "is designed to train the individual to decide how much information he needs and how little he needs, to give him a sense of balance and proportion." In the term of cybernetics theorists, culture is a "total information system"—open or closed, depending upon the precise conditions of the culture at any time.

Throughout history the framework of this organism changes only slightly; what do change frequently are the conduits for the flow of information. Does information move from the periphery to the center, from the center outward, or in full circuit? Is information considered a static, precious commodity, treasured and guarded against change? Or does it depend on change for its value to the culture? Do the conduits of information tend to move into ever-enlarging areas, pressing the borders of a culture further outward, or do they encircle themselves, locking knowledge into a tight area? New media dictate the directions cultures take, Innis says; they are the principle of change in a world of relative constants.

Homeostasis is the organic process by which the body maintains an equilibrium of energy resources. It ensures that the energy from food and oxygen reaches all parts of the body. If an arm becomes diseased, white corpuscles from other parts of the body collect in the arm to fight the invasion. Innis depicts the action of balanced media in culture as a means of guaranteeing a cultural homeostasis—an equilibrium of the unstable forces that threaten at every stage to wreck civilization. His use of the time and space biases carries overtones of Adam Smith's "invisible hand." Empires, Innis writes, "have tended to flourish under conditions in which the civilization reflects the influence of more than one medium and in which the bias of one medium toward centralization is offset by the bias of another medium toward decentralization."

Time and space, for Innis, are essentially measuring devices. He uses these two polarized categories to test the effects of a certain medium upon a culture. The crucial question is: how does a new medium contribute to the process of homeostasis—or, overcoming it, wreck the culture and establish a new one? Here Innis's economic background is especially important. Not unlike Mumford and other historians, Innis views the introduction of a new medium as a response rather than as pure and simple innovation. The world had to be ready for script, for parchment, for the printing press; and ready in the sense that the established forms of power had gone too far, had upset the delicate balance, and required the challenge of a new medium. The Church maintained its awesome power in the Middle Ages largely through its ability to convince the populace of the innate authority of the written word—*its* written word. Such a hegemony of power forced a reaction—a reaction not only of men, but of a new form of communication, the printing press. Luther used the printing press far more wisely and more effectively than the Catholic hierarchy he fought. This is invariably the case: insurgents turn to new media with the instinctive knowledge that these media can be used with greater power than was ever suspected. Innis shrewdly notes that both printing press and paper had been available to the Chinese for centuries; but the Chinese had a much more stable base of power (in effect, a balanced ratio of time and space biases) and the wider uses were never required.

Such a theory of the "invisible hand" in media and culture contains some fine ironies. Censorship, for example, which is usually concentrated on the uses of the dominant media in a culture, encourages an insurgent group to search out a new medium where the censorship controls do not yet exist. On the other hand, "freedom of the press" is the best guarantee that the nationalistic mentality and the present power structures will thrive—almost regardless of what the press *says*. New information does not necessarily threaten an ensconsed power elite. But a new medium for information does.

The seesaw of culture dips and rises, then, as a result of the entrance of new media and the decay of older forms. Equilibrium is the desired position, but it is rare. The history of civilizations is a history of excesses—war, economic injustices, social aggravations reaching their climax in revolution. Mediation and moderation belong to ethical theory, only occasionally to history. Innis suggests that the media provide better mechanisms for achieving equilibrium than the men who use them. But Innis knows better than most that media are always conditioned by their culture, their period, and their uses.

Every new technology, he points out, is first applied, successfully or not, to communication. The alphabet was quickly desacralized and used in commerce in Greece, Ethiopia, and Mesopotamia. The printing press was the first device to use numerous interchangeable parts and follow mechanized, repeated motions; it heralded the industrial revolution by three hundred years. The first major use of electronics was in the telegraph. Technology contributes to the competitive thrust of media more quickly than to any other needs—including food or shelter, which would seem to be more vital.

"The bias of communication" is, therefore, a central dynamic of history. Buckminster Fuller insists that men and institutions can only be changed after the environments are changed. Harold Innis shows how the changing controls of information—the media—have triggered the rise and fall of empires—from Byzantium to the Church's empire in the Middle Ages. The monopoly of knowledge established by a medium is the foundation of power and the key to history.

But to better understand exactly what he means, we must examine Innis's key terms more closely—"empire" and "monopoly of knowledge."

TO SUBVERT AN EMPIRE

Not the least of Innis's difficulties for his readers is his occasional abstruseness. "Monopoly of knowledge," one of his favorite expressions, is a good example. Does he mean by this phrase *who* controls the knowledge? Is he referring to the media in which the knowledge is contained and through which it flows? Does the monopoly consist of the *mode* of knowledge, such as oral or printed knowledge? Or does "monopoly of knowledge" work as the equivalent of a "monopoly of resources"—an elastic economic term in which the controlling factor could shift from geography to a wealthy class to government?

Judging from context, Innis seems to use the term on all

these levels. In one instance "monopoly of knowledge" is used in regard to the priestly class in Egypt; in another instance to the geographical range of the Roman empire. The phrase, while one of Innis's most important, is likewise one of his least specifically defined. Innis anticipates McLuhan not only in ideas, but in the frequent ambiguity of his phrases.

"Monopoly of knowledge" appears always to include three factors: the constriction to one medium, the limitation of a certain *form* of knowledge, and fairly tight control by a small power hegemony. For example, the dominance of print has meant first of all that only printed kinds of knowledge are granted as essentially valid. As a consequence, knowledge must adapt to the contours and demands of print-oriented power institutions: for example, probably no institution has shaped education in America so thoroughly as the textbook publishers. As Philip W. Carey in his commentary on Innis states, "Only knowledge that conformed to the concerns and cultural predispositions of the dominant medium would persist. In a written tradition, knowledge must be technical, secular, and future-oriented for it to be defined as legitimate or recognized as valid." Moreover, the established powers—in this case the universities and educational establishments—are fundamentally incapable of permitting an intrusion by any other form of knowledge. The monopoly of knowledge protects its own with wary vigilance.

For Innis, a monopoly of knowledge empowers and sustains empire. Empire denotes to him the ability of a civilization to maintain control over vast stretches of space or time, or both. Empire is "an indication of the efficiency of communication. It will reflect to an important extent the efficiency of particular media of communication and its possibilities in creating conditions favorable to creative thought."

Innis's book, *Empire and Communication*, develops this theory of empire by showing the conflicts between different media within the major civilizations since Sumer. Empires are incomplete (or dominated by their particular "bias") unless somehow the opposite bias is assimilated and a balance is achieved. The *true* history of civilization, Innis suggests, would follow those rare and relatively brief periods when balance and stability dominated the culture. "Dependence on clay in Sumerian civilization was offset by dependence on stone in Babylon and a long period of relative stability followed in the reign of the Kassite. The power of the oral tradition in Greece which checked the bias of a written medium supported a brief period of cultural activity such as has never been equaled. Dependence on the papyrus roll and use of the alphabet in the bureaucracy of the Roman Empire was offset by dependence on parchment codes in the church and a balance was maintained in the Byzantine Empire until 1453 . . ."

Empire, then, does not necessarily mean the conquest of space, but can likewise mean the control of time. Ideally—Innis's measure of the greatness of any empire—it means both.

Two fundamental problems of empire absorb Innis: how it is created and how it is maintained. Media, certainly, provide the key mechanisms for establishing a new empire, and the monopoly of knowledge guarantees continuation. Yet both media and the monopolies of knowledge they create work within and through a volatile complex of interacting forces. Innis's writings become dizzying when describing this interaction. How, briefly, does empire come about?

To begin, any culture already has some dominant medium and therefore its own monopoly of knowledge. Before a new medium can successfully enter the culture, some disturbance must take place. Quite often this disturbance will consist in the failure or limitation of the present communications bias. The early Sumerian dependence on clay, for example, created a stratified religious society in which contact with other, more progressive, cultures like the Egyptians and Semites led to a recognition of the inefficiency of damp clay as a writing medium. A tighter and more flexible alphabet was the first outcome of this tension; but finally a fusion with the Semitic culture, based on the medium of stone, forged the Babylonian empire. Eventually the Babylonian empire itself, based on tablets of hard clay and hieroglyphs, was exposed to the competition of papyrus—a newer, more efficient medium. The weakened fabric of Babylon left it at the mercy of the Assyrians, who invaded in 729 B.C. and finally destroyed the city in 689 B.C. When the old medium is in the process of giving way to a new medium, the culture reaches its most dangerous stage of instability.

The introduction of a new medium, says Innis, rarely threatens the established order at first. When the Babylonians saw papyrus, they recognized its advantages and began using it before they became aware of its dangers. The introduction of paper into Europe in the twelfth century hardly provoked the opposition that its use for promulgating the vernacular did two centuries later. A new medium enters an old order subversively. Only its appeal is visible, not its optimum possibilities. Such is the story, as Mumford, Giedion, and Ellul would have it, of all new technologies.

What or who, finally, controls the process whereby a new medium comes to dominate a culture? Where the evidence is available (and before modern times this is rare), the process seems almost self-sustaining. New media are created or borrowed according to a culture's needs. A stratified, religious civilization such as the Babylonians' was governed by a strong temporal bias—tablets of clay are durable but too heavy for wide distribution. The stronger the bias, the greater the need for its corrective: in this case a lighter, more portable medium —such as papyrus. The farther the pendulum swings to one side, the greater the force with which it will swing back.

Once introduced into a culture, a new medium immediately makes its users conscious of its advantages over the old medium. A tension ensues. The Greeks at the time of Plato were torn between the advantages of oral discourse, with its freedom, its personal responsibility, its dialogic possibilities, and writing, with its promise of a permanent record and its potential for a broader education. Plato's own writings reflect the tension in their dialogic structure, yet they also reflect Plato's attempt to impress upon the dialogues an order that may not have existed in conversation. Aristotle, a student of Plato, resolved the conflict, breaking completely from the dialogue format and organizing his writings with a consciousness never possible before print. Writing formalizes content. It likewise gives the writer a larger voice—historically or geographically—than was possible for the orator.

Monopolies of knowledge give power to unique structures of authority. Law and bureaucracy were necessary, for example, in the Roman Empire, but depended upon the papyrus codex to such an extent that the Christian oral tradition was able to supplant it. Since the forms of every culture become translated into the heritage of their successors (a phenomenon similar to Mumford's "cultural pseudomorph"), law and bureaucracy became important features in the Church after Constantine. But the translation from papyrus to parchment concentrated the direction, bending the Church inward and committing it to time, away from the spatial conception of the Romans.

The success of empire requires not only the subversion of an older medium and its monopoly of knowledge, but the means of maintaining the new monopoly of knowledge. These means will differ according to the bias of a culture. Innis suggests four basic ways in which control and authority over an empire are secured: systems for storing and continuing knowledge (libraries and schools), organizations capable of dealing with the distinct features of the cultural bias (in a spatial culture, bureaucracy and law; in a temporal culture, a strong religious force); regulations to check the advance of newer media, or forms of knowledge not controlled by the culture's monopoly (censorship is an ostensible example, "freedom of the press" a subtler one); and, most important, the cultural conditioning that enables everyone to accept the boundaries imposed by the dominant medium. The first three of these means are apparent. The fourth deserves further attention.

A dominant medium is the dominant environment. As McLuhan reminds us, and as we have previously noted, its very pervasiveness makes it invisible. The culture, by virtue of the pervasive domination of a medium and it bias, tends to condition everyone to accept and live out the bias. "Propaganda is any culture in action," says Ellul; and the propagandizing effects of a culture are nowhere more totalizing for Innis than in the temporal or spatial bias. People in a spatially oriented culture, for example, will prefer painting, with its spatial, flat appeal, to sculpture; people within a temporally oriented culture, like the Greeks, prefer the permanence of a pose or action caught in sculpture. Democracy is the great myth of a spatially oriented culture; a life beyond death that of the temporal culture. Spatial cultures are ahistorical, with the concomitant peril: "The essence of living in the moment and for the moment is to banish all individual continuity." The Egyptians, one of the greatest of time-bent civilizations, built pyramids in which space literally closed at a point, the apex. The monuments of contemporary Western civilization are highways spanning continents. The function of secondary environments—whether communications media, forms of travel or production, educational or religious organizations—is invariably to reflect and further promote the bias of a civilization.

Control, therefore, in Innis's interpretation, does not assume a simple complex of political or economic mechanisms; authority springs from a civilization's spatial or temporal bias. Innis considers the greatest weakness of any civilization to be its inability to suspect, challenge, and confront the dominant medium and its bias. At one point he quotes Harold Laski: "The most important service rendered by the press and the magazines is that of educating people to approach printed matter with distrust." We are too much a part of a print culture today to begin to understand, Innis suggests, how profoundly print has affected our lives.

Such a manipulatory description of authority gives Innis's work a slightly deterministic overcast. But when the dynamics of interaction are as complex and unpredictable as Innis shows, even the primary biases of space and time become loose forces within a field of shifting figures and events. Innis avoids a stringent depiction of time and space as totalistic, unmediated forces. Least deterministic of all is his description of those rare phases in history where the time bias and the space bias have been balanced.

There are two kinds of cultural stability. The first is that of raw force, where the culture maintains its bias by legislating and enforcing it. Roman law and military power guaranteed the persistence of the empire's spatial bias. In the thirteenth and fourteenth centuries the Church fought the rise of the vernacular by exerting fierce censorship. A stability of force is defensive and guarded: an unacknowledged insecurity founded upon the extremity of a spatial or temporal bias. The structural strength of a stability of force is like that of a crustacean—the whole is supported by a rigid, brittle outer shell; one slit can weaken and eventually destroy the entire shell.

The second method of stability is equilibrium, which results from a balance of the time and space biases, as epitomized in the culture of classical Greece. There the strong oral sensibility fused successfully with the new demands of writing so that, for example, "the writings of Plato enabled him to dominate the history of the West." Balance gives a culture a sense of wholeness and interrelatedness. Creativity and social harmony result. The competition between state and religion, between the moral and the technical, and between art and science tend to be constructive, not harmful. In Greece, the oral tradition flourished as a written tradition slowly entered, permitting a new equilibrium and a period of astounding vitality and cultural health. Only after the fourth century B.C. did the written tradition overcome the oral bias and give way to a splintering individualism that spelled the decline of classical Greece.

The stability guaranteed by a temporal-spatial balance is for Innis the norm of any civilization; hence his comments on the growing spatial bias of the modern West are grim. Since the introduction of paper into Europe in the twelfth century, Western civilization has been moving away from a temporal bias and toward an exaggerated spatial bent, more severe and one-sided than that of any previous civilization. The two critical events after paper for promoting the spatial bias are the printing press and the mechanization of paper production and printing. Each step has led Western man further into a spatial universe, where the monopoly of the eye is all-powerful. The latest step in this process—mechanization—has led to new kinds of control mechanisms. "The large-scale mechanization of knowledge is characterized by imperfect competition and the active creation of monopolies in language which prevent understanding and hasten appeals to force."

Mechanization of the printing process intensifies the visual-spatial bias and provides it with a new justification: commercialism. Innis's paper, "Technology and Public Opinion in the United States," a careful study of the growth of raw-edged journalism, shows that newspapers promote the very factors that gave birth to them: mechanization, mass production, commercialism. Commercialism is the apotheosis of the spatial bias. "It is at this point that the tragedy of modern culture has arisen as innovations in commercialism have destroyed a sense of time."

Throughout history, values have always been at the mercy of the principal bias in a culture. For the Greeks, with their careful balance of oral and written traditions, virtue is knowledge; for the Hebrew prophets, members of one of the strongest temporally bent oligarchies in history, knowledge is dangerous, as it entails new responsibilities. Each bias favors those values that shaped it and maintain it. Thus in a spatial culture life is secular, physically unbounded, nationalistic, scientific, materialistic, individualistic. In a temporal culture, religious values such as community, faith in an afterlife, reverence for tradition, and a suspicion of material gain predominate. In any culture, both sets of values will operate, one as a dominant force, the other recessively. What Innis suggests is that we have entered a period in which the recessive virtues of a temporal bias have all but disappeared. Man has been cast into a universe of the now, where his only frontier is physical distance. Even time has been spatialized, so that man regards the future as another physical frontier to be conquered. Innis sees glimpses of hope in the competition of radio, and the "linking of sound to the cinema and to television." But for all practical purposes his writings conclude at the dawn of the new media. The work of his disciple, Herbert Marshall McLuhan, would later begin where Innis left off.

THE BIAS OF HAROLD ADAMS INNIS

What kind of a history is this, where libraries outscale emperors and the difference between papyrus and parchment means more than the difference between war and peace? Innis is fascinated with civilization not as the story of man, but as the rise and collapse of information systems. If the monasteries from the sixth through the twelfth centuries hoarded virtually all the manuscripts west of Byzantium, wouldn't that, in the final count, make more of a difference than who was Pope, or what social system dominated the land? Innis does not claim that ideas are always the instigators of change, but he does assume that they are indispensable for civilization. And what makes a civilization unique are the ways in which ideas move, are contained, get transmitted through time and space, and become shaped by their movements into unique patterns of thought and action. The history of civilization follows only a step behind the history of media.

Innis's contribution to a total understanding of man's relationship to his environments is a major one: original in its thrust, unlimited in scope, and highly complex in its dynamics, Innis's theory has posed assumptions distinctly different from other environmentalists such as Mumford and Ellul. The interface process for Innis happens only over stretches of time and space; and it will be important only when the environments are media of communications. Mumford points to the clock as the undergirding structure of the industrial revolution. Innis not only points to the printing press, but he suggests that the industrial revolution is only one aspect of an overwhelming spatial bias, that is really the thrust of modern civilization. Moreover, where Mumford, Giedion, and Ellul assume that man interacts *with* his technologies, Innis suggests that man interacts *through* the new media-environments, in the process restructuring the bias of a society, or the major invisible environment. Here Innis might seem closest to Ellul, who emphasized the invisible nature of technique. But bias transcends technique. A bias means two things: a cultural prejudice or predisposition; and a control mechanism that guarantees the movement and storage of information in such a way as to further extend and enforce the bias. Technique may work through prejudices and may create control mechanisms (though Ellul says little of this). But Ellul envisions technique as a larger, more malevolent force than a bias—as, almost, a conscious principle of technology.

Innis adds significantly to Ellul—as well as Mumford and Giedion—in suggesting the profoundly environmental nature of man's most decisive technologies, his media of communication. The environment is not what surrounds us, Innis suggests, but what quietly controls our relationships with one another. By altering a culture's attitudes toward space and time, a medium like parchment or print reroutes man's information ecology—at once stabilizing a culture and making it vulnerable to disruption from a new medium.

Harold Innis has made two major contributions to an understanding of cultural environments and how they work. He has proposed what could be called a "cybernetic" theory of history and environments, and he has explored what may be the two richest categories for investigating the impact of the media: time and space.

Norbert Wiener defines cybernetics as "the study of messages as a means of controlling machinery and society." The term comes from the Greek word *kubernetes,* meaning "steersman." Wiener himself was more interested in the structure of messages than in the media they used. Yet Innis and Wiener agree on the general notion that information controls society.

How did Innis view the relationship between media and their content? Might he have coined the phrase, "The medium is the message"? Probably not, for he did not conceive of media and information as a form-content relationship. Innis's frame of reference was chiefly economic; in it, forms are everything. After all, what is the content of money? For Innis, information was not content, but the theoretical constant in the flux of changing media. Innis approached culture much as a designer might approach buildings in which the electrical circuits have been altered. What implications do new relationships of circuitry have for the occupants and the processes of a building?

Much of Innis's contribution lies in his influence on Marshall McLuhan, who called *The Gutenberg Galaxy* a "footnote to the work of Harold Innis." It becomes quickly apparent, reading McLuhan's works, how profound is his debt to the economist who first raised the questions that McLuhan later pursued.

On the first reading, similarities between McLuhan and Innis appear more striking than the disparities. Both men are concerned with the significance of media for culture. Both use a wealth of resources that cut across academic boundary lines. Both write in a jammed, enigmatic style studded with brilliant insights. Both Innis and McLuhan share a preference for oral over visual cultures, and look (if in differing degrees) to the new world of electronic communications as a return to an aurally based world.

Yet differences abound as well, many of them substantial. McLuhan shucks off Innis's categories of time and space, choosing rather the direct sensory bias—a bias hinted at in Innis's later essays, but never really developed. The difference can be seen in their respective interpretations of the late medieval period. For Innis the introduction of paper gave rise to the vernacular and disseminated information far beyond its earlier, monastically oriented boundaries. McLuhan sees no particular significance here, except perhaps an early preparation for the printing press, which would give the eye full dominion over the ear.

James W. Carey states in his essay, "Harold Adams Innis and Marshall McLuhan," that the fundamental difference between Innis and McLuhan lies in Innis's concentration on the institutional effects of media, and McLuhan's on perceptual and psychic effects. This is only half true. Innis uses institutions as handy reference points, but he seems just as interested in the psychic effects of new media. "A writing age was an egoistic age." "Disappearance of the spirit of music was followed by the decline of tragedy."

Innis emphasized institutions because the historical record could back up his judgments. Few critics of Innis have charged him, as they have charged McLuhan, with a misreading of literature, or with irresponsible interpretations of the history of art.

A subtler difference between Innis and McLuhan lies in their conceptions of environments and the way in which environmental processes can be illuminated. For McLuhan, environments become visible not as much by their effects as by their interaction with other environments. "Learning creates ignorance. White creates black. The public creates privacy." Language as a formal structure did not become apparent until language had become "the content" of print, thus creating literacy and bad grammar. Innis takes a quite different route. The major environments become visible through the reshuffling of power within the structures of a society. Their effects go beyond this but it is to these changes that Innis looks for clues. No doubt one reason Innis did not carry his work beyond the turn of the twentieth century is that his method requires historical evidence and perspective.

Innis shares with McLuhan one of the ultimate criticisms of the kind of ideas both men have put forth: but how can you prove it? The difficulty with quantum logic is that it builds upon gaps—big ones. One finds conclusions, but never tenets, in every sentence of Innis's. It was not he but McLuhan who defended Innis's method and style. If, writes McLuhan, they were "to be translated into perspective prose, it would not only require huge space, but the insight into the modes of interplay among the forms of organization would be lost. Innis sacrificed point of view and prestige to his sense of the urgent need for insight."

Gaps pervade the work of both men. Innis identifies causes and effects, but rarely the mechanisms that link them. The omission makes it hard to adapt Innis's thesis to the contemporary situation; consequently, McLuhan had to take a different approach to the basic ways in which media change society. Perhaps the largest gap of all is Innis's failure to articulate a total theory of what he was doing. He left only an outline, with roughed-out sketches from which a more comprehensive theory might be extrapolated.

Perhaps nowhere else do Innis and McLuhan agree as well as in their orientation toward the oral tradition. The bias of contemporary civilization may be spatial; but the bias of Harold Adams Innis is decidedly oral. Innis's interpretation of the West after Gutenberg is pervaded by a somber sense of loss. Printing created a monopoly of the eye and introduced to the West an array of evils ranging from nationalism to commercialism. But Innis discerns in radio, film, and television a return to oral media that might mean (he seems to waver on this point) a vitality in culture similar to that of the Greeks, who successfully merged an oral tradition with a written alphabet.

Innis sensed, as McLuhan would after him, that oral media are healthier for culture than any others. An oral tradition and, consequently, an oral sensibility are interpersonal rather than impersonal. It tends toward immediate and local forms of authority over distant, centralized forms, it encourages dialogue rather than a monopoly of opinion and keeps the world alive with magic and a sense of mystery, it makes learning an involving and creative activity rather than a simple experience of information transmission. Most important, however, is the contact that the oral tradition has with the organic. If the oral bias is completely lost, man becomes totally dependent on media external to himself. Written words, with their high degree of denotation, kill connotation, and thus restrict feeling, instinct, song. "Students of linguistics," writes Innis, "have suggested that the spoken word was in its origins a half-way house between singing and speech, an outlet for intense feelings rather than intelligible expression." The loss of oral communication is for Innis the loss of man's touch with himself.

The vision of Harold Adams Innis is too rich, too varied, to bound to its own eccentric medium for successful synopsis in these few pages. He was the first to propose that media are our most important environments and yet the least visible. Alfred North Whitehead has written that "The major advances of civilization are processes that all but wreck the societies in which they occur." Innis has added an important epitaph: out of the wreckage comes a society capable of reacting to the worst extremes of the old order—but endangered by its own bias toward the very opposite extremes. Media can liberate or confine man; just knowing that may one day make the difference.

EIGHT

The Sage of Aquarius

MARSHALL McLUHAN

> I am in the position of Louis Pasteur telling doctors that the greatest enemy was quite invisible, and quite unrecognized by them. Our conventional response to all media, namely that it is how they are used that counts, is the numb stance of a technological idiot. For the "content" of a medium is like the juicy piece of meat carried by the burglar to distract the watchdog of the mind. The effect of the medium is made strong and intense just because it is given another medium as "content." The content of a movie is a novel or a play or an opera. The effect of the movie form is not related to its program content.
>
> Marshall McLuhan,
> *Understanding Media*

Harold Innis quietly introduced a fresh way of interpreting the role of media in history. Indeed, his work has provided historians and cultural anthropologists with a fresh yardstick by which to study the nature of social change. But what began as a signal insight for Innis has been modified, reorganized, and elaborated into cosmic proportions by his greatest disciple, Herbert Marshall McLuhan.

The work of Harold Innis raised more questions than Innis ever answered. Are the time and space biases the only criteria by which we can judge the effects of media in society, or are they the only two that Innis had chosen to explore? As media involve more and different kinds of technologies, do their modes of influence change accordingly? Would electronic media create such an overt spatial bias that no new medium *could* offset its effects?

McLuhan's work appears as more of a departure from Innis than an attempt to resolve its questions. Indeed, McLuhan drew from Innis little more than a fundamental way of approaching media and Innis's dense, elliptical method for dealing with the subject. Innis's most important theories—the time-space tension in history, the function of media in usurping or supporting various kinds of authority, the relationship between media and organizations—do not appear in McLuhan's work except in the most tangential way. *The Gutenberg Galaxy,* the book by McLuhan that is closest to Innis's thought, and that McLuhan himself considers a footnote to Innis, carries a premise that Innis would have approved—the printing press as the focal event in recent history—into areas that might have surprised Innis as much as anyone else, for example, the notion of linearity and "linear thought" as a fundamental feature of post-print culture.

There can be no question that McLuhan owes a great deal to Innis. The two were good friends for several years, and McLuhan never hesitates to point to Innis as *the* pioneer in these questions, but apart from certin similarities and parallel developments that I will point out directly, the two men have followed different courses and have reached different conclusions.

Herbert Marshall McLuhan is a native Canadian. Born in Edmonton, Alberta, in 1911, he spent most of his boyhood in Winnipeg and studied at the University of Manitoba. His doctoral studies at Cambridge brought him into contact with I. A. Richards and F. R. Leavis, whose critical techniques can be seen reflected in McLuhan's later writings, particularly in his shrewd analysis of ad copy in *The Mechanical Bride.* He taught at the University of Wisconsin (1936-1937), St. Louis University (1937-1944), and Assumption University in Windsor (1944-1946) before joining the faculty of St. Michael's College, University of Toronto, where he has taught since.

McLuhan's writings have increased, ironically, with the development of his analysis of a typographic culture and his fascination with the electronic "post-Gutenberg" technologies. Throughout the Forties he wrote primarily for literary journals, though by the mid-Forties his subject matter had taken on the topics of popular culture: comic strips, popular novels, radio shows. In 1951 his first book appeared, *The Mechanical Bride*, perhaps to this day the single most important book published on popular culture. While *The Mechanical Bride* emphasized the content of ads, comic books, comic strips, *Time* magazine, and similar material, McLuhan already recognized the importance of form. He considered, for example, the front page of *The New York Times* a "symbolist landscape," evoking the sense of a space-time continuum of relativity physics.

As much as it seems to represent an auspicious beginning, *The Mechanical Bride* actually signaled the end of a period in McLuhan's career. Never again would he concentrate on "content" quite so emphatically, or with the rude tone that suggested the familiar moralistic stance taken by the literati toward popular media and advertising.

McLuhan's second book, *The Gutenberg Galaxy* (1962), is a landmark. Many critics consider it his finest and most important book, combining a major idea with enough scholarship to give it at least the merit of a passing credence. The book emerges from much of McLuhan's work over the previous decade: his chair in a Ford Foundation seminar on culture and communication, the eight issues of a little but important magazine called *Explorations in Communication,* and a steady movement toward a major theory of communication media. In *The Gutenberg Galaxy* McLuhan sets forth his theory that the typographic culture sparked by Gutenberg has drastically altered man's way of perceiving the world, bringing in its wake nationalism, individualism, the breakdown of the churches, and generally all the other ills experienced by Western man since the Renaissance and Reformation. The book is organized in brief, barely related chapters with cryptic titles such as "Heidegger surfboards along on the electronic wave as triumphantly as Descartes rode the mechanical wave."

McLuhan's next book endowed him with the dubious distinction of being Pop Philosopher of the Sixties. *Understanding Media* (1964) originated from a grant by the National Association of Educational Broadcasters. McLuhan intended the book as a sequel to *The Gutenberg Galaxy,* an attempt to trace the psychic and social consequences of electronic technology, much as he had traced those of the printing press. But lacking the historical perspective of four centuries, McLuhan was forced to draw his evidence from every source of contemporary life. Thus he buttresses his thesis with *MAD* magazine, Jack Parr's television style, two-inch news stories from *The New York Times,* and comments on a variety of phenomena from disc jockeys to miniskirts.

Understanding Media, with its somewhat scrambled thesis, its shaggy, overwhelming prose, and its almost intoxicated delight with the new electronic environment, brought on a torrent of criticism. Dwight MacDonald, for example, commented: "A single page is impressive, two are 'stimulating,' five raise serious doubts, ten confirm them, and long before the hardy reader has staggered to page 359 the accumulation of contradictions, non-sequiturs, facts that are distorted and facts that are not facts, exaggerations, and chronic rhetorical vagueness has numbed him to the insights."

Yet *Understanding Media* did more than anything else to

transform McLuhan into the "oracle of the electric age." There is no questioning the appeal that McLuhan's thought holds for advertising writers, business executives, network chiefs. Not only had McLuhan recognized the drastic new form that communications had taken; he saw in it the promise of a new Eden, or to use his own phrase, a "global village." The oracle, a title questionably deserved, seemed to be playing favorites. Indeed, he seemed to justify the whole complex of new technologies, while giving special sanction to the beast itself—television.

Acclaim led to controversy, and the controversy flamed about as long as McLuhan's popularity. But what the controversy, and more importantly the overnight acclaim, tended to obscure was the lasting value and significance of McLuhan's thought.

McLuhan's later books reflect two tendencies: a more popular exegesis of his thought in *The Medium Is the Massage* (1967) and *War and Peace in the Global Village* (1968), and the further development of various pet themes in *Through the Vanishing Point* (1968), and the function of advertising as a form of cultural homeostasis in *Culture Is Our Business* (1970).

McLuhan's books, particularly his two most important ones, *The Gutenberg Galaxy* and *Understanding Media,* obviously lack the organization, the thoroughness, and the clear systematic structure of Mumford, Giedion, or Ellul. Indeed, one of the largest problems McLuhan poses to his reader is that of method. His writing, vacillating between the oracular and the cryptic, can be as difficult as that of Innis, though quite often far less opaque.

McLuhan has defended his method, or lack of coherent method, by calling his thought "probes." "For me any one of these little gestures I make are all tentative probes. That's why I feel free to make them sound as outrageous or extreme as possible. Until you make it extreme, the probe is not very efficient . . . Of course they *sound* very dogmatic. That doesn't mean you are committed to them." It is a handy enough tactic, but essentially a ruse. McLuhan's thought, by and large, does coalesce into a system. And he is, like most system-builders, more dogmatic about it than he will admit. If McLuhan's thought comprised nothing *but* probes, and if McLuhan took them all with the scant seriousness that he avows when discussing his "probe" method, he never would have achieved the large-scale theory that he has developed, nor would he have kept it.

You might say that there are three notable qualities to McLuhan's method: his attempt to engage the reader "aurally," or through oral-aural techniques; his unique constructions of logic, though these often represent deteriorated forms of older logic; and his essential playfulness with the reader.

In his method, as in his thought, McLuhan is reacting consciously to the period of eye-dominated, linear "typographic man" that is being dispelled by the new electronic media. Alphabet and print have fostered habits of thought such as differentiation, classification, and the single point of view. The logic of typographic man is extended and consistent. McLuhan will have none of that. Although he does use recognizable logic, and although his thought is still "linear" to the degree that he writes in sentences, the reader suspects that McLuhan feels more partial to an oral, discursive mode of writing. Ideas jump in every direction. The idea at the beginning of a paragraph has shifted in meaning and implication by the conclusion of the paragraph. McLuhan does not delineate a subject so much as trek around its perimeters, commenting on the interaction between that subject and others. As such his writing resembles nothing as much as a high-intensity brainstorm session. "Does General Motors, for example, know, or even suspect, anything about the effect of the TV image on the use of motorcars?" McLuhan calls this the substitution of insight for logic. But it seems closer to the familiar tactic of any shrewd conversationalist: hit on an idea that, right or wrong, jars your listener into reacting.

McLuhan's oral-aural emphasis emerges in many of the features that his critics have found so perverse. His epigrams are examples: "We march backwards into the future"; "politics offers yesterday's answer to today's questions"; "the medium is the message." He also has pet phrases, sometimes used almost as incantations: "global village," "acoustic space," "hot medium," "cool medium." These are oral tactics, more familiar to a speaker than to a writer.

The most distressing oral-aural ploy of McLuhan's for the modern reader, however, is no doubt his lively use of hyperbole. In *The Presence of the Word* Walter Ong has pointed out that one of the important innovations that print made in the history of thought was to curtail hyperbole. Overstatement is a valid and necessary conversational technique. If two people sit down to discuss a question, the discussion will lack direction, force, and above all, energy unless they overstate, to some degree, their ideas. Much of McLuhan's thought should be considered intentional overstatement. When he says, for example, that the psychic effects of television are virtually unrelated to its content but stem entirely from the form, he is orally stating (which means overstating) the idea that the medium affects us through its very structure and perceptual bias. His own comments on what succeeds in television content and what does not suggest that he does not believe that TV content is totally insignificant; he simply wants to emphasize the form against the content.

Harold Innis's approach to the organization and relationships between historical data has been called "quantum logic"—indeed, the phrase is McLuhan's. He has adopted the technique from Innis, and he uses it often much in the same way that Innis did, making enormous jumps within single sentences and leaving the reader to figure out what causal connection, if any, exists. "The ordinary classroom still holds the typewriter at bay," states McLuhan. And, he says almost purely in Innis's vein, "The same urge to translate the tactile skills of the older crafts into the visual magnificence of the Renaissance rituals provided an aesthetic medievalism in the North, and in Italy inspired the recreation of ancient art, letters and architecture." Perhaps the only critical difference between McLuhan's quantum logic and that of Innis is that McLuhan has injected a new energy level and shown new preference for generalization and overstatement.

Quantum logic is really not so much a method of logic as a convenient way of dispensing with slower forms of logic to make a drastic point quickly. Innis used it to avoid the dangers of slipping into an easy chronology or losing touch with his real subject. McLuhan has honed it to a fine instrument, and elicited from it three derivative forms: what might be called "pendulum logic," "creation-by-awareness," and metaphor-as-proof.

Pendulum logic is simply an application of Innis's historical approach. The dialectical streak in McLuhan is not so pronounced as it is in Innis, but when it appears it seems to take on an even greater validity for McLuhan than it did for Innis. For example, McLuhan sees the conflict of old and new technologies not simply as a process of subversion, but an actual war, resulting in large social and psychic violence. The pendulum that swung to print four hundred years ago has swung back with even greater force, now that television has appeared. No one knows what makes the pendulum swing, but with McLuhan it swings wider, betokening more hazards for the culture.

McLuhan's method of interpreting the cultural impact of a new medium often follows a unique route—his logic of "creation by awareness." The central idea here is highly important to McLuhan's whole thesis, namely that once a new medium has altered our perceptions, we begin to recognize new entities, things that were there all the time, perhaps, but that now take on a fresh significance within the new social or psychic framework sparked by the medium. For example, he notes that people became aware of language structure only after the printing press; before the printing press there was no such thing as "bad grammar." Sometimes this method is concentrated into a cryptic phrase, such as "Black creates white," or "Learning creates ignorance." McLuhan uses this technique to explain one of his favorite insights: why the old environment becomes the content of the new environment—why movies, for example, did not become popularly recognized as an art form until the appearance of television.

Metaphors, McLuhan has avowed, transform and transmit experience; indeed, "all media are active metaphors in their power to translate experience into new forms." Metaphors collect in McLuhan's work like "therefores" in the *Summa Theologica*. McLuhan, rarely at a loss for evidence of sorts to buttress his theories, often resorts to metaphors. In explaining the process whereby our technological extensions numb us to the effects that they are having upon us, McLuhan calls upon the myth of Narcissus, who fell in love with his own reflection. Before the reader realizes it, McLuhan has dubbed the phenomenon "Narcissus narcosis," and—despite the use of other evidence, such as Hans Selye's work with stress—the Narcissus metaphor has become the most vigorous argument for the process that it describes.

Ultimately, McLuhan's method fails to give thorough validity to his theories. But one suspects that McLuhan is not interested in validity; he would rather charge the reader, challenge him, provoke him to think about his environments as he has never thought before. And here, by and large, McLuhan is successful. For his method becomes games that McLuhan plays with his reader. He will supply a dozen excuses for his method: Observation is better than experimentation, because you do not disturb the phenomenon; moral evaluation, implicit in any concentration on content, would only upset the real work of understanding environments; formal methods of logic cannot be applied to these questions, because they are included in the very criticism these questions attempt. But largely these are ploys, chances to slide a rock across the board without its being spotted. McLuhan's method, much as its content, has about it a tone of playfulness, of fun. But even that is a larger ploy, a summons to the reader to reach the core ideas and recognize how urgent and upsetting they are. McLuhan, whatever his limits as a historian, writer, or even philosopher, cannot be faulted too easily as a shrewd and canny teacher.

A NEW DOMINION

In the interpretation of Harold Innis, media maintained their dominion over civilizations by predisposing cultures toward spatial or temporal forms of organization and institutions. While McLuhan neither agrees nor disagrees specifically with Innis's theory, he clearly has learned from it. What McLuhan proposes is a similar but even more radical interpretation, a dominion of media over cultures, but a new dominion, one in which media affect civilization not through spatial or temporal biases, but by modifying the human sensorium.

The difference between the two theories cuts deeper than it might first appear. Innis leaves the process of media shaping culture outside of man, a process as invisible as it is inaccessible. McLuhan centers the process within man, rooting the changes in his perceptions, locating the bias not in a spatial or temporal proclivity, but in the unrecognized dominion of one sense over the others.

It should be noted that both Innis and McLuhan give man at best a passive role in their theories. For Innis, man develops, through his institutions and social structures, the bias that the medium insinuates into the culture. McLuhan's interpretation is in this sense more disturbing, for he places man at the center of the process, while giving him no role in initiating or controlling it. The linear, visual modality created by the printing press acts *upon* man; the conditioning is powerful, inescapable, and imperceptible. Critics have charged McLuhan with disinterring Locke's *tabula rasa,* the mind as a blank tablet, and using it for his own purposes. Actually, McLuhan is describing man more as a creature programmed by his environment to perceive and act in certain ways, while being incapable of recognizing that he is being programmed.

The process of the "sensory dominion" in history can be seen over four broad periods: the oral, tribal period; the age of writing; the civilization created by print; and the new configuration that springs from electric circuitry, what McLuhan calls the "global village." The key to each period is its unique sensory ratio, the result of the dominant medium.

Like Innis, McLuhan favors an oral-aural world. (Though, I suspect, for different reasons: Innis seems to recognize the political advantages of an oral culture, such as decentralized government. McLuhan's reasons seem to be more aesthetic.) In describing the tribal or "acoustic" environment of pre-literate peoples, McLuhan emphasizes the quality of life created by the ear, rather than the social structures or psychic consequences resulting from an aural bias.

The ear is man's tribal sense. Primitive, filled with personal levels of energy and emotion, its power is instinctive and magical. Before the alphabet and the visual reference patterns it established, man lived in acoustical space, space without boundaries, perspective, or visual qualities, space defined by emotions rather than its visual dynamics.

In an oral culture, sounds contain their meaning; the word for an animal sounds like the animal. Feeling and thought are the same. Information systems, unavailable in print, must be contained within men's minds, making memory all-important, fostering poetry, myth, and a surprising degree of personal knowledge. Despite the tribal context of oral man, McLuhan argues that he has more individuality, more freedom than typographic man, whose individualism tends to be a segment of a larger social pattern.

McLuhan professes greater faith not only in the organic character of an oral people, but in their perceptions. It is, he writes, "quite obvious that most civilized people are crude and numb in their perceptions compared with the hyperesthesia of aural and auditory cultures." Spoken words are alive, can change, remain close to their root meanings. Written words, however, tend to be locked into a single meaning. Moreover, the spoken word favors an infinite variety of expressive nuances. Oral words favor fresh perception; written words favor preconception. A pet McLuhan exercise is playing with word origins. Freshly minted words—up until the recent phenomenon of bureaucratic word production, such as "itemize" and "de-escalate"—reflect the dominant perceptions of the people who created them. Philology is a quick route into the mind and perceptual world of an oral culture.

The shift from an oral to a visual culture was precipitated by the early Greeks, who introduced the first alphabet in which characters had barely vestigial visual relationships to the sounds they represented. (Cuneiform and hieroglyphic writing, in contrast, was more representational than symbolic.) The cultural shift has been documented most thoroughly by Eric Havelock in his *Preface to Plato*. Plato's attacks on poetry have traditionally baffled readers and scholars alike.

Havelock shows that Plato, desiring an education and in effect a society built upon literate, stored knowledge, was attacking the preliterate *need* for poetry, based upon an oral tradition.

Writing and print are two stages in the evolution of the same phenomenon: a medium that fosters perspective, linear thinking, segmentation—in effect, a monopoly of the eye. McLuhan cites the Greek myth of Cadmus, who brought the alphabet to man but ended up sowing dragon's teeth that sprang from the earth as armed men. Writing "translated man out of the possessive world of total interdependence and interrelation that is the auditory network." It changes the pattern of learning, fostering preconception over perception. "The discovery of the alphabet will create forgetfulness in the learners' souls," said Socrates in the *Phaedrus*. "You will give your disciples not truth but the semblance of truth; they will be heroes of many things, and will have learned nothing; they will appear to be omniscient and will generally know nothing."

Print survived, and two thousand years later became further codified, further disseminated through the printing press. Whereas the shift from oral to written media was the major historical event for Innis, McLuhan interprets the typographic revolution as being far more important. Print transformed the culture as no medium before had. By establishing a total supremacy of the eye, it shattered the old eye-ear equilibrium, and thrust man into an entirely visual universe. The book, the source of post-Gutenberg education, encouraged an intimate communication between man and print; its linear mode, its portability, its totally visual quality entrenched modern man in an individualistic, spatial universe. And the very commonness of books transformed their content. Ong has shown that Peter Ramus, one of the most important popularizers of the transformations begun by print, tended to regard knowledge as a commodity rather than as wisdom.

McLuhan considers the monopoly of any one sense as precipitous, the causeway to cultural stupor. "The dominance of one sense is the formula for hypnosis," he writes. "And a culture can be locked in the sleep of any one sense." Print not only apotheosized the eye; it eclipsed the possibilities of other senses, holding them into a pattern that only further guaranteed visual supremacy. In terms of Innis's theory of history, the monopoly of print had reached a point where it invited a challenger. With the introduction of electronic media, print would not only encounter a conflicting form of communication, but one that subverted its visual monopoly.

Understanding Media, in which McLuhan explores the psychic and social repercussions of electronic media, is structured on the premise that television represents for our age and for the near future roughly what the printing press represented for the last four hundred years. The phrases "before television" and "after television" run like twin motifs through the pages. Indeed, one of the central methods McLuhan uses is to suggest how television has changed various other technologies such as toys, automobiles, airplanes, and speech. He sees television as the apex and apotheosis of the electronic revolution. In many contexts the two terms, television and electronic media, become inseparable.

Nowhere are McLuhan's claims for a single medium as vast and as contrary to experience and common sense as his interpretation of television. Television, he argues, is not a hot medium like radio, movies, and print; indeed, it is the coolest medium known to history. It involves the viewer, engages him in in-depth participation, and substitutes his linear, print-developed mentality for a non-linear, tactile sensibility. According to McLuhan we do not watch television; we reach out and touch it.

The television screen is a configuration of light patterns formed by the dots along 525 lines. A scanning beam, what

McLuhan calls the "scanning finger," shoots electrons across a phosphor screen. The interaction of the electrons and the cathode tube gives both form and movement, or the *effect* of a picture. (Whether a television image consists of a picture or not is a fascinating question; if you try to photograph that "picture" at the wrong *f*-stop on a camera, you will see the scanning beam, but not much picture.)

What we see, therefore, is not a completed picture, but a very incomplete one, related to a photograph about as vaguely as a comic strip relates to a finely crafted Dutch painting. The key to television's tactile quality is that the viewer has to fill in the picture. The process is so instinctive and immediate as to be unconscious, but nonetheless it forms the perceptual relationship between an individual and a television screen. Whereas the direct, linear process of print pressing itself on the eyes tends to be overtly visual, the demanding, incomplete, television image tends to be subtly tactile.

When McLuhan says that television is an "in-depth" experience, he is not referring to the demands it makes upon intelligence, but rather to the viewer's action of completing, filling in the image. To understand television, we must understand tactility. "To the sense of touch, 'all things are sudden, counter, original, spare, strange.' "

McLuhan argues that the tactile bias established by television has already affected our culture noticeably. Pattern recognition displaces logic; systems design and systems analysis replace older, more linear, managerial and organizational forms; the one-thing-at-a-time principle of baseball gives way to the sudden, all-at-once character of football; mesh stockings and see-through blouses replace "overdress"; politics shifts from a war of precincts and policies to one of Madison Avenue techniques.

Kenneth Boulding has commented of McLuhan, "It is perhaps typical of very creative minds that they hit very large nails not quite on the head." While this statement applies well to all of McLuhan's thought, nowhere is it more apropos than in his interpretation of television as a tactile medium. The two ideas—that television affects us most profoundly regardless of its content, and that we do not "watch" TV as much as "touch" it—run directly counter to our experience of television. And while our experience may be misleading us (many of Freud's theories run counter to the lesson of experience) it appears that strictly on the basis of solid evidence McLuhan has failed to assemble a convincing argument. Is television tactile because we do not get as complete a picture as we do in a photograph? Is color television less tactile than black-and-white TV? According to McLuhan it should be, because the colors, at least with good reception, provide far better definition than the mottled grays of a black-and-white image.

And yet one cannot help feeling that McLuhan has hit the right nail; he just has not hit it on the head. The problem that vexed Mumford, that discouraged Innis from carrying his observations into the new media, is back to plague McLuhan: To what extent can you interpose the methods that worked in interpreting past history upon present experience? McLuhan insists that the monopoly of the eye that dominated Western culture since the sixteenth century is now being shattered by the electronic media. Somehow electronics *are* changing our world—and ourselves—in a far more considerable way than anyone cares to admit. McLuhan is raising the question as no one has quite raised it before, and even in failing to answer it adequately, he shows just how important the question is. The cultural transitions of recent years, from pattern-recognition as an intellectual method to miniskirts, are large and drastic, and McLuhan has made more sense of them than anyone else. The tribal life-style of hippies seems almost a de facto response to McLuhan's predictions of a new tribalism. Only in explaining the exact process, and in focusing it so singly on television, has McLuhan foundered.

Innis did not bother to examine the processes by which the bias of a medium became translated into a culture. McLuhan, unquestionably more intrepid than his mentor, has attempted to examine the process.

He identifies three steps. The first of these is the creation of a new technology, which McLuhan sees as the extension of some human organ or activity. Before him Buckminster Fuller and Edward Hall had stressed the extension principle: that the car extends the foot; the rifle extends the hand; the radio extends the tongue. *Understanding Media* is subtitled "The Extensions of Man," and McLuhan emphasizes that these extensions must be considered together, not as separate, distinct forms, but as an environmental version of man's whole, interdependent organism. For McLuhan, the whole is not even comparable to the sum of its parts. The extensions of man are the technological exaggerations of all that man is.

Yet the extensions of man—his environments—always adhere to some pattern, some way of emphasizing a certain organ. Thus in Greek culture before Plato the ear gave the environment its distinct quality, its strong aural bias. The introduction of a new technology into the culture alters this pattern, producing a transformation of the environment. Since environments are always invisible, this change can be grasped only in its effects. Thus in *The Gutenberg Galaxy* McLuhan comments on the introduction of written symbols into the aural Greek world: "The interiorization of the phonetic alphabet translates man from the magical world of the ear to the neutral visual world."

In *Understanding Media,* however, McLuhan digs deeper into the process and describes the other two steps. He calls the second the "Narcissus narcosis." Narcissus, he says, looked into the water and mistook his reflection for someone else. "The extension of himself by mirror numbed his perceptions until he became the servomechanism of his own extended or repeated image." Having fallen in love with the "someone else" who was actually himself, he lost the ability to perceive things—most important, himself—as they were. McLuhan comments wryly, "Obviously he would have had very different feelings about the image had he known it was an extension or repetition of himself."

"Narcissus narcosis" is the shock of recognition that results in numbness. McLuhan draws upon Hans Selye's work with stress. In cases of severe stress or irritation, Selye has observed, the body reacts with a simulated amputation. The boxer battered too long in the shoulder eventually loses his sense of pain in the shoulder; his body has been forced to neglect or "amputate" the shoulder. A new technology is both caused by and causes "Narcissus narcosis." The quickened pace in exchanging "written and monetary media" in early civilizations created an extension of acceleration and movement. The irritation this caused demanded a counter-irritant, or an "autoamputation," the wheel.

This second step of the process is the most complex. The extension of one feature causes a numbing "blindness" to the real character of the extension; it likewise forces, either immediately or eventually, an autoamputation—another extension that can act as a counter-irritant. Even as we encounter a technology new to our environment, we immediately numb ourselves to it. "Precisely at the point where a new media-induced environment becomes all-pervasive and transmogrifies our sensory balance, it also becomes invisible."

The process of Narcissus narcosis reaches its apex, McLuhan states, with electronic technology, which is an extension not simply of one organ, but of the entire nervous system. Each new technology is a response to the buffeting effects of an older one—McLuhan's adaptation of Innis's theory of new media subverting old ones. Electricity arrives, therefore, by way of the printing press. "It could well be that the successive mechanizations of the various physical organs since the invention of printing have made too violent and superstimulated a social experience for the central nervous system to endure."

The third step in the process likewise involves an adaptation from Innis. Cultures reached their apex of creativity and vitality, said Innis, when the interaction of media permitted the two biases to counterbalance one another. Interplay between media (and consequently between the sensory biases created by the media) is likewise for McLuhan the basis for the most vital points of cultural history. McLuhan's version of history is a study of the backwashes of those explosions that are the critical junctures between two interacting media. "Of all the great hybrid unions that breed furious release of energy and change, there is none to surpass the meeting of literate and oral cultures. The giving to man of an eye for an ear by phonetic literacy is, socially and politically, probably the most radical explosion that can occur in any social structure . . ."

A dominant medium not only shapes man's sensory environment but serves as the index to the powers of that environment. The extent of its power can be felt in the shock waves emanating from collision with a new medium. Where Innis speaks of subversion, McLuhan speaks of direct conflict. Indeed, war between nations or cultures as we know it is nothing more than the most graphic and bloody effect of a new technology encountering an old one. "The one inexorable consequence of any identity quest generated by environmental upheaval is tremendous violence."

No matter how powerful environments are, McLuhan says, it is dangerous to succumb to them without being aware of what is happening.

The dominion of distinct sensory monopolies that the media impose upon history can be seen as a distinct corollary to Innis's theory. However, McLuhan suggests that the influence of the media tends to be broader and more profound than Innis ever implied. For McLuhan no phenomenon, whether a comic strip or a major war, has significance outside of his system. Indeed, it seems to be one of the more impressive features of his systems that it can provide an alternative explanation for virtually any event or innovation.

A McLUHAN LEXICON

The previous section has followed the major periods of history as McLuhan interprets them, through the major shifts in media and consequently in perceptual biases. Another way to get into McLuhan is to scrutinize his unique vocabulary. McLuhan enlists specific words and phrases and gives them fresh, if often elusive, meanings. An analysis of these words and phrases and the meanings that McLuhan has given to them can help with that sometimes maddening, always enticing, effort of Finding Out What McLuhan Is Really Saying.

ACOUSTIC SPACE

Aural man inhabits a spatial universe without distinct boundaries, without center, without margins. "Acoustic space is organic and integral, perceived through the simultaneous interplay of all the senses. . . . The man of the tribal world led a complex, kaleidoscopic life precisely because the ear, unlike the eye, cannot be focused and is synaesthetic rather than analytical and linear." Acoustic space emphasizes the subconscious over the conscious, the magical and mythical over the scientific and logical. E. S. Carpenter wrote that

Eskimos "don't regard space as static, and therefore measurable; hence, they have no formal units of spatial measurement, just as they have no uniform divisions of time. The carver is indifferent to the demands of the optical eye; he lets each piece fill its own space, create its own world, without reference to background or anything external to it."

McLuhan contrasts acoustic space to visual, or organized space, the universe inhabited by visual man. The critical difference between the two is that in acoustic space qualities of space are determined by the suggestive, mysterious character of hearing; in pictorial space, the imposition of organization and coherence by the eye make space linear, limited, above all enclosed. (*Cf.* pictorial space.)

COOL/HOT

In his introduction to the paperback edition of *Understanding Media,* McLuhan notes that "hot" used to mean intense and involved, whereas "cool" meant detached and disinterested. McLuhan claims that lately the terms have reversed their meanings, though he seems to be the source of this reversal.

A "cool" medium, such as speech or television, is one that requires the involvement of several or all of a person's senses. The information is low in definition, demanding that the person "fill in the gaps," or as McLuhan would put it, "warm it up." In reading a comic strip, for example, we see only outlines and the briefest shapes that we must "fill in." A hot medium such as movies or radio provides us with information that is already highly defined and that usually appeals to one sense. McLuhan uses the hot or cool nature of a medium much as Innis used the spatial or temporal bias of a medium: to gauge its social effects.

DEPTH, IN-DEPTH

McLuhan uses some words metaphorically, and his use of "depth" or "in-depth" illustrates this well. Usually employed in connection with "cool," "involved" media, "depth" is the opposite of a linear, sequential orientation. It connotes a totality of relationship and inner, sometimes instinctual participation. McLuhan implies, though he never quite states, that depth experiences tend to be emotionally involving, not simply cerebral, as, for example, print tends to be.

ENVIRONMENT

McLuhan uses the term "environment" in three ways: (a) in the familiar sense, meaning the immediate sensory world; (b) as media, for example the television environment; (c) most importantly and most originally, as an unseen sensorium emerging from the new media, a pattern of involving and altering certain sensory ratios. The third meaning lies at the center of his theory of environments, and will be developed later in this chapter.

GLOBAL VILLAGE

The circuitry of the new communications media spans the globe, making information instantly available to everyone. Television has reintegrated the old fragmentations of the print universe, and created a single organic megaculture, which is tribal in character. McLuhan has terms this megaculture a "Global Village." His term is less oblique than Teilhard de Chardin's "noosphere," but more vulnerable to criticism. Of McLuhan's phrases, it is the most metaphorical, and perhaps for that reason among the least helpful.

INVOLVEMENT

McLuhan uses the term involvement descriptively to refer to the mode of participation or interplay between an individual and a medium. McLuhan's use of the term gives it connotations it usually does not have, and he limits its precise meaning. For example, he considers radio a "hot" medium, and therefore not very involving. The fact that a radio drama "involves" our imagination more than a television drama will not fit into McLuhan's use of the term. An involving experience is profoundly social, and creates tribal sensibilities.

MEDIUM

McLuhan goes much further than Innis in conceptualizing media: any conduit for information or transportation (both of these words, in turn, defined quite broadly). Thus *Understanding Media* includes clocks, bicycles, typewriters, weapons, computers. Since McLuhan's main concentration is on the *form* of a medium and the way in which that form alters sensory ratios, the content of media is not, as was generally thought until McLuhan, their chief defining characteristic.

PICTORIAL SPACE

Whereas acoustic space reflects an aural intuition of the world, pictorial space reflects a visual conception. Pictorial space is enclosed, limited, constructed around centers. The use of perspective in Renaissance art, with a painting or a building leading in toward the "vanishing point," reflects a total internalization of pictorial space.

ROLE

McLuhan frequently contrasts role and identity, or role and job. Basically the word "role" refers to the specific way in which a person relates to a single situation. McLuhan considers roles as forms of in-depth involvement, as against jobs, which are specialist and uninvolving.

SYNAESTHESIA

The *Random House Dictionary* defines synaesthesia as "a sensation produced in one modality when a stimulus is applied to another modality, as when the hearing of a certain sound induces the visualization of a certain color." McLuhan suggests a slightly different meaning—a sensory interplay in which the experience of, say, aural and visual information (as in a rock concert) tends to become so distinct and unusual as to become tactile—for McLuhan, the most profound and involving of the senses. In effect, synaesthesia is for McLuhan a combination of senses that become tactility.

TACTILITY

By tactility McLuhan means two interrelated phenomena: (a) touch, the only sense not associated with a particular organ, and man's closest experience of his central nervous system; (b) synaesthesia, or a combination of senses. As synaesthesia, tactility represents for McLuhan the best harmony of the senses possible; it was familiar to tribal man, and to the Greeks before Plato, but its supple balance has been overthrown by literacy.

TRIBAL

One of McLuhan's major contentions is that man, as a result of electronic media, is returning to the sensibilities of his pre-literate ancestors: a profoundly social, non-individualized, and in-depth existence. Tribal man, McLuhan avers, prefers costume to uniform, chooses wholes over specialized parts, inhabits a world of acoustic as opposed to pictorial space. Tribal man is essentially aural or tactile; indeed, McLuhan suggests, the main difference between early tribal existence and post-electronic tribal existence will be the shift from an aural to a tactile sensory bias.

AN ELECTRIC EDEN?

Like Innis, McLuhan has attempted in his writings to avoid what he calls the "fixed point of view," and its concomitant tendency to pronounce value judgments on the phenomena he is interpreting. McLuhan claims that value judgments obscure the real work of interpreting these phenomena. Yet he speaks blithely of untold psychic effects of "overheating" the cool television image, of the possibility of engineering national and cultural moods by controlling radio and television sources, of the immense cultural *value* of advertising—arguing that only when people are preoccupied with "the threat of scaly scalp, hairy legs, sluggish bowels, saggy breasts," can there truly be democratic freedom.

Such observations reveal not only a highly deterministic conception of the new media, but for McLuhan's critics suggest that he sees the new technologies as man's freeway to a new, electric Eden. McLuhan has frequently made comments that support his idea. In *Understanding Media,* for example, he states, "Electricity points the way to an extension of the process of consciousness itself, on a world scale, and without any verbalization whatsoever. Such a state of collective awareness may have been the preverbal condition of man."

Indeed, it is perhaps the most common criticism of McLuhan that he sees in the electric media the promise of an infinitely brighter, richer world; one in which the tribal village overrides national feelings and wars; in which consumption and the dependence on new technologies become something akin to an act of virtue; and in which consciousness itself is elevated by the mysterious workings of electricity without, as one critic has put it, the intervention of consciousness.

In effect, McLuhan has been identified by many critics and readers as the major apologist of the corporate, television-dominated society, promising in our literally blind subservience to it a new, totally electric Eden.

The argument is a valid one. McLuhan often does describe the future in terms that betray a mood of extreme optimism, if not sometimes euphoria. And he does suggest that the way in which we can best relate to the electric media is to submit to them. "Electromagnetic technology requires utter human docility and quiescence of meditation such as befits an organism who now wears its brain outside its skull and its nerves outside its hide. Man must serve his electronic technology with the same servomechanistic fidelity with which he served his coracle, his canoe, his typography and other extensions of his physical organs."

McLuhan may not promise a utopia in any classical sense; his terms are vague, his vision lacks the patterned articulation of other utopian schemata. But as James Carey and John Quirk have suggested in "The Mythos of the Electronic Revolution," McLuhan can be seen as a contemporary equivalent of a distinct American tradition, the apologists of a technological Eden.

This tradition, which Leo Marx calls "the rhetoric of the technological sublime," flourished in the mid-nineteenth century. Thomas Jefferson looked to urban skills and technologies as the source of great vitality and wealth for the nation. Despite some misgivings, Emerson prophesied a union of machinery and transcendentalism. Even as late as the turn of the century, when the corrupting and dehumanizing effects of industrialism were glaringly apparent, major writers such as William Dean Howells and Edward Bellamy heralded the age of electricity as man's salvation.

And McLuhan? He can be coaxed into the position of apologist and prophet of an electric Eden; his shaggy, multi-directional writings supply enough passages to fortify, if not justify, such an interpretation. But it is doubly unfortunate that McLuhan has been relegated to this position. For even though he does *appear* optimistic about electricity in much of his writing, he has likewise expressed profound doubts and fears that his critics have chosen to ignore. But more important, the question of an electric Eden tends to reconstruct McLuhan's thought around that position. And with McLuhan it is less a position than an attempt to suggest the radical difference between a print-shaped culture and an electrically shaped culture.

Much of it comes down to a problem of misinterpretation. When McLuhan uses a phrase like "global village," he is not speaking literally—even as a metaphor the term founders—but aphoristically. In other words, the term has meaning only within its context, and for the purpose of conveying what McLuhan hopes to emphasize by the context. And what McLuhan usually means is the all-at-once, world-encompassing character of electronic technologies as opposed to print technologies. "Today the globe has shrunk in the wash with speeded-up information movement from all directions. We have come, as it were, to live in a global village. Our information comes at high speed, electronic speed from all quarters. We would seem to be living, almost under early conditions, in a small village world."

Given the problem of some of his passages, and given McLuhan's tendency to get carried away at times, does not his basic thesis suggest that we are entering a new Eden of sorts, where man once again will experience a harmony of his senses due to the aural-tactile nature of electric media?

Here McLuhan *does* postulate an improved condition for man after electric technologies. But this is something quite distinct from a defense of corporations, television content, and advertising. McLuhan, much as Innis, personally favors an aural over a visual universe. It is less a profession of specific values with McLuhan than a personal tendency, a natural faith in the fidelity and richness of aural over visual experience. And McLuhan anticipates, as a result of the electric media, a return to an aural-tactile world of the senses, one that encourages greater social harmony and breaks down the old individualisms and specialisms of the West. Yet what of the political and industrial dangers that such new media introduce? What about the power of a small number of people to condition and even manipulate vast numbers through electric media? McLuhan avoids such questions assiduously. He claims, and here he may be right, that the executives at the major networks have no idea what they are doing, no idea what the television medium is all about. He has recommended that, since the clash between the electric culture and the print culture has reached such ferment, we slow down and turn off the televisions for a decade or so. But otherwise he has shown little in the way of answers as to how we can reach his promised Eden without being waylaid into some electric Brave New World.

And here lies a major criticism of McLuhan. It is not that he has postulated an electric Eden, but that he has shown no ultimate distinction between a genuine harmony between men, based on trust and community, and an imposed harmony, based on the skillful manipulation of new electric media, from television to electrodes fastened to the skull that may one day keep people happy, tribal, and hopelessly stupefied. One suspects that the basic values undergirding Mc-

Luhan's work are aesthetic in nature rather than moral. That McLuhan can brilliantly explore the repercussions of a visual or an aural bias, much as a painter or a musician explores his environment, is not questioned, but rather that deeper moral questions leave him uninterested, and perhaps unconcerned. What Innis kept so consciously alive in his interpretation of history McLuhan has virtually ignored—namely the human uses of power, and the inevitable tendency for men to take advantage of the powers that media exert over men and society.

McLUHAN AS SEEN THROUGH A REAR-VIEW MIRROR

We see only the recent environments, McLuhan claims, as they rush away from us, as though through a rear-view mirror. It is one of his more apt metaphors. But it likewise applies to any attempt to pin down McLuhan. One feels that he can only criticize McLuhan using the techniques and linear modes of thought that characterized an earlier era. Given his assumptions, McLuhan can move around with boisterous energy, misstating facts, leaving central theories supported with only tatters of evidence, combining ingenious insights with extravagant hyperboles—and tell his critics that he is only making probes, that in an electric age one must suspend judgment and attempt above all to understand.

McLuhan has so craftily combined the brilliant and the original with the preposterous that his thought requires, more than that of anyone else in this volume, careful critical examination. The notion that the medium is the message opens up important new ways of interpreting print, radio, and other communication technologies. But when McLuhan applies it to the light bulb, claiming that it is another medium, and insists that the "content" of such a medium is whatever happens in its glow, from surgery to a baseball game, the idea seems stretched beyond its proportions, and indeed, tends to invalidate the genius of his more basic idea.

"Nothing exceeds like excess," McLuhan has remarked. He should know. Faults are not only prevalent in his work; invariably they become more critical because they are so excessive. He abuses facts with a consistency and even an adroitness that leads the knowing reader to believe that McLuhan has no real interest in things as they are but in things as they can be construed to support his interpretation. He overextends and sometimes grossly changes the meanings of terms. His use of "involvement," for example, assumes either that imagination and intelligence have no play in a person's interaction with a medium, or that they serve only to obscure the real process of sensory subjection.

In his critique of *The Gutenberg Galaxy,* Frank Kermode has commented of McLuhan that he is faced with "an insoluble problem of method. Typography has made us incapable of knowing and discoursing otherwise than by a 'metamorphosis of situations into a fixed point of view'; that is, we reduce everything to the linear and successive, as computers reduce everything to a series of either-ors." In effect, McLuhan cannot validly criticize the typographic method while at the same time depending on it. He is like a man attempting to explain the bias and constrictions of a language while being able to speak only that language. This does not invalidate McLuhan's argument. But it does show the difficulties of trying to grapple with it and locate methods of testing it.

There are innumerable other problems in McLuhan's method, such as his use of poets and novelists, from Shakespeare to Joyce, to buttress a specific point. He claims, for example, that Shakespeare "understood the forest of Arden as an advance model of the age of automation, when all things are translatable into anything else that is desired." There is McLuhan's tendency to explain anything as a consequence of his interpretation of media in history. The Vietnam war thus becomes not a conflict between nations or ideologies but the by-product of the new American technologies conflicting with the tribal life style of the Indochina peninsula.

Yet the most important criticisms of McLuhan do not attack his method as much as his message. I have already commented upon his glorified idea of the tribal village, the Eden of a television-reared, tactile culture. Two related problems deserve attention: his view of man as the composite of his senses, and his elusive but treacherous determinism.

It seems surprising that for a man who has constructed a system of thought as vast and daringly original as McLuhan's, he would be so weak in that central area where the most important processes take place, namely, psychology. Experimental psychologists have long neglected the problem of man's interfaces with his environment; McLuhan reciprocates by neglecting all human consciousness and activity other than the sensory interplay with the environment. McLuhan suggests that man's personality is shaped more decisively by his environments than by any other single factor, and yet these environments are invariably impersonal, acting upon man not through their content but irrespective of it. What of human relationships? The human or dehumanizing content of the media? He suggests that the only factor that matters in our involvement with media is the nature of the sensory interplay with those media. Does this mean that time spent watching "Captain Kangaroo" is just as beneficial as time spent watching a new documentary? McLuhan, ultimately, posits little or no principle of intelligence at work in our relationship with the media; it is not so much what we see but how we see or hear or touch. The medium is the massage.

But that leads to a psychology of sorts and, more disturbingly, an implicit determinism more threatening to human freedom and human life than the grim spectre of Ellul's technique. If we are being massaged by every medium, if our personalities, our cultural forms, our institutions, are the passive materials for invisible forces that massage and mold away, what can we do to ensure control of our environment short of curbing all media and therefore all communication? McLuhan makes no proposals; nor does he modify his thesis to include some other principle of interaction with media beyond the purely sensory involvement.

It is clear that McLuhan, in extending his aphoristic, hyperbolic technique into his theory, has cloaked his gems well. He has made it impossible for us to accept him whole; and though the temptation may be strong to disregard him whole, that would be an equally unfortunate mistake. The man's work is rich, studded with insights and surprises, and poses major questions that themselves reflect the stabbing accuracy of genius. The method McLuhan claims he uses—pattern recognition, as against the linear, one-after-another technique—might best be used for reading him.

McLuhan's contributions can scarcely be judged yet; over time, they may influence psychology, perceptual studies, sociology, anthropology, and various other sciences. Within the context of this volume, however, McLuhan's contributions are striking. By positing a principle of organic continuity between man and his technologies, McLuhan has shown some way of reconciling the ultimate technological problem of value. Moreover, he has developed the most comprehensive theory of environments yet, explaining not only how environments interact with man, but describing a process of continuity between environments, through the old environment becoming the content of the new one. He has explored important questions such as the distinction between mechanical and electronic technologies. Partly by his own failures he has helped illuminate the value of Innis's work, at the same time taking Innis's ideas and exploring their significance in fresh ways.

Most of McLuhan's theories may, over time, collapse; he is too incorrect too often to be his own best apologist. Yet no one can deny that McLuhan may be the greatest gadfly of our age; opening doors that would otherwise have gone untouched, despite his own tendency to stumble once inside.

PART III

Vortices of the New Ecology

NINE

Engineering the Future

> Our own utopian renaissance receives its impetus from a desire to extend the mastery of man over nature. Its greatest vigor stems from a dissatisfaction with the limitations of man's existing control over his physical environment. Its greatest threat consists precisely in its potential as a means for extending the control of man over man.
>
> Robert Boguslaw, *The New Utopians*

In the scant two hundred years since the early Industrial Revolution, Western man has totally rescaled and changed the face and fabric of his environment. Indeed, the changes have proceeded at such an accelerated pace that we might use the word "old" or "outmoded" to refer to last month's computer model.

But as Mumford has pointed out so well, the changes thrust upon our civilization by technology have been anything but planned. The close alliance between technology and business has led to a succession of environmental accretions that are sporadic, unorganized, and often unbalanced. The overlay of problems facing any large city testifies to our inability to organize our technologies nearly as well as we can devise new ones.

Previous scientific thought built on what the information theorist Warren Weaver has called "linear or one-way causality." An experiment in biology or physics was designed with everything controlled but one factor—permitting the latter to reveal the causal mechanism. This method cannot be applied to the design of new urban centers or the development of ecological safeguards in the Everglades. Where a range of factors are at play at once, and there is neither the time nor the means for using the old one-way method, a new kind of method—indeed, a new scale of thought about the problem—becomes necessary. Systems design, known also as systems analysis, systems engineering, and operations research, is fast replacing the old scientific model in many of the social sciences as well as business and government.

In systems design and systems research, the whole is more than the sum of its parts; the ecosystem (total environment) becomes more than a container for the forms within it. Systems design, at least as a theoretical model for approaching contemporary problems, is thoroughly environmental—in the argot of Buckminster Fuller, "synergetic."

Systems design has already made a significant impact on the behavioral, social, and natural sciences. In biology it has aided (and been aided by) ecology, ethology, and bionics. In psychology it has helped challenge the behaviorism of Watson and Skinner, leading toward an "open system" interpretation of human behavior; and it is, as Ludwig von Bertalanffy has remarked, "the most discussed notion in present sociology."

The theory of systems design can be seen in two spheres: in the efforts of social engineers, as a means of modifying the environment more drastically than ever before; and in the newly emerged science of cybernetics, of which Norbert Wiener is the leading exponent. Buckminster Fuller, while not strictly a systems designer, has been proposing a science of comprehensive, anticipatory design that incorporates—and in some ways pushes to new extremes—the fundamental tenets of systems analysis.

THE ENGINEERED ENVIRONMENT

If organization is the first postulate of the systems designers, then control is the second. The men whose ideas we have considered so far have been analysts, historians, theorists, and interpreters. They have perceived and described environmental conditions, but have not contributed toward building them. Men like Norbert Wiener and Buckminster Fuller are less interested in analysis than in constructing new environments, or at least the methods for these new environments. Their most striking feature is that they propose to design these environments whole. The seeds of mankind's life style in the twenty-first century may be found in their thought.

Systems design is more a mode of thought than a label that can be applied to any particular school or group. There are frontier areas in which systems design has been carried further than elsewhere: for example, simulation gaming, urban design, managerial organization, and traffic control. But the importance of systems can be seen more in the structure and assumptions within systems design itself than in any particular uses of systems design within specific situations.

There is, to begin, a significant difference between a systems *design* and a science that deals with already existing systems. The ecologists is less interested in designing a new system than in preserving a present ecosystem—whether a valley, a lake bottom, or a river. Most natural systems, from the chemistry of the cell to an Arctic plain, have evolved without any active collaboration on the part of man. The work of systems designers is to change a present system—or, more increasingly, to create a totally new system that can be applied to specific problems.

Systems designers use the terms open (or "dynamic") system and closed system. An open system, like the human body or a healthy ecosystem, is dynamic: constantly in flux, changing, capable of adapting to new circumstances and new demands. A closed system, like an automobile or an automatic elevator system, cannot change or adapt; it can only respond to stimuli in terms of the factors that have been designed into it. The terms open and closed systems become less distinctive in the case of business organizations, bureaucracies, and certain games, where features of both open and closed systems are apparent.

The application of systems design to various problems has revealed three major features—each of which suggests how drastically systems design promises to change our environment. These could be called the holistic outlook, the importance of multiple control factors, and the tendency toward quantification. The holistic outlook is immediately apparent within any systems design. A traffic controller about to reroute major traffic patterns by switching to one-way streets and adding traffic lights cannot begin to focus on a solution without first understanding the gestalt—the major arteries in and out of the city, the location of bottlenecks, the directions taken by the heaviest and lightest traffic at certain hours. The systems designer is concerned above all with wholes. The value seemingly implicit here, that the parts must give way to the greater advantage of the whole, is less a doctrine of social conformity than a necessary premise to the successful design of a new whole. Admittedly, this emphasis makes it difficult for the systems designer to permit room for local variations. A systems designer can include presently existing local variations into his system; it is much more difficult—in some cases impossible—to leave a system open-ended enough so that local variations can emerge separate from the programming tendencies of the system.

By virtue of its holistic conception, any system must be conceived and developed in relation to other systems—in its own scale or of a larger, more comprehensive scale. It is impossible to design a city without considering the factors of import and export, or the terrain, or neighboring cities, of transportation into and out of the city, etc. A tendency exists within systems design that leads toward ever-larger systems, increasingly more scopic and totalistic in outlook. A hint of the furthest reach of this tendency can be found in Buckminster Fuller, who argues for a comprehensive, anticipatory design science of global proportions.

A systems designer or systems engineer is somewhat in the position of the juggler who has to keep six balls in the air at the same time. If one ball drops, an attempt to catch it might involve losing several other balls. To keep his balls in the air, the juggler requires an ability to handle what the systems designers might call multiple control factors. In other words, you can't control a system with one handle. You must deal with several factors at once, and your control exists only to the extent that you can maintain a harmonious balance of these controls. An automobile driver needs only to swerve the wheel a little, or shift gears at the wrong speed, or jam on the brakes over a slippery surface to endanger the total system—himself, the automobile, and any passengers.

The characteristic of multiple control factors makes it difficult for any system to change easily or even to be controlled easily—or to be accessible to control and change. A government bureaucracy, which is a semi-open, semi-closed system, is virtually impossible to manage effectively because the control factors are so numerous and so inaccessible. Even when the control factors are within the operational reach of a tight organization, such as NASA, the possibility of error exists—as could be seen from the near-fatal flight of Apollo 13.

The third characteristic of systems—the quantification of variables—is less a characteristic of all systems than a tendency toward which systems move, particularly those in which computers are used. Systems design is not necessarily mathematical in its initial phases, but as the amount of information required to design a system mounts, the need to organize and assess that information leads almost always toward the computer—and toward the quantification of information. For example, consider the problem of a man who must determine the route of a new highway through a city. After the political and economic considerations have been taken into account, he must choose between several alternate routes, with no clear answer as to which route best satisfies the various needs involved: economy, not ruining present traffic patterns, avoiding the political assault of a threatened neighborhood, etc. He might choose the route by finding out which areas have cohesive community ties that would be imperiled by the highway. Or he might try to reduce the problem to quantitative variables—such as the property values and the relative demolition costs. The tendency in situations where computers are available and where the information lends itself to easy quantification is to make the choice on a quantitative basis.

Systems designers pride themselves on the inherent neutrality of their work. Whether they are planning a dam, designing a city park, or organizing the food distribution for an underdeveloped nation, they approach the activity with the sole idea of making something *work*. If they perceive any values in what they are doing, these tend to be vaguely utopian values—the notion that they are designing a somewhat better world. Robert Boguslaw has shown how the utopian disposition of many systems designers and engineers tends to lead toward an even broader attempt to apply new systems. But generally systems designers are less utopians than farsighted technicians—the critical difference being that the utopian is obsessed with his vision, and the technician wants to make something work.

Yet there are utopians among the systems designers; Buckminster Fuller has attempted, to some degree successfully, to make the concepts of global systems design and utopia synonymous. Perhaps the most striking example of the utopian tradition among the systems designers is the movement toward futurism, or anticipating, and therefore learning better to control and organize the developments of the coming epoch.

The futurists have a twin interest: in the "organized prophecy" that is made possible by sophisticated methods such as the "Delphi" technique of forecasting; and in designing systems to control, relate to, utilize, develop, and even subdue the trends that have been forecast. While the enterprise of futurism may seem no more than an updated version of the shawled gypsy leaning over her crystal ball—who, after all, is qualified for prediction?— the new futurists are more than crystal-ball gazers. The Rand Corporation has made recommendations affecting government spending in the billions—recommendations made with an eye cocked confidently toward a highly forecasted future.

The futurists consider H. G. Wells the first of the modern thinkers dealing in "organized prophecy." Wells was perhaps the first modern writer to grasp the social implications of technological innovation, looking to major technological advances, particularly in transportation, as the single key element for transforming a society. Wells, however, did not consider technological patterns, or more important, social systems—many aspects of which (such as religion) specifically resisted the influence of new technologies.

More recent futurist studies have followed a range of predications and predictions. Bertrand de Jouvenal, a French *Futurible,* argues for a methodology by which valid assumptions about the future can be made; he has a more mathematically oriented American counterpart in the Rand Corporation's Delphi projection study summarized in Olaf Helmer's *Social Technology.*

The Year 2000, by Herman Kahn and Anthony J. Wiener,

interprets the future as a continuation of presently visible trends—in city expansion, computer centralization, industrial growth. The possible specific orientations of these trends are regarded as alternatives (or "scenarios") for further prediction of social consequences. Kahn and Wiener present the futurist enterprise as a complex game in which the player pauses after each move to judge its overall effect on all the pieces on the board. Computer-based games are a basic resource of the Hudson Institute, a management "vision" center, and *The Year 2000* is one result of Kahn's and Wiener's work there.

The major trend in futurist studies (de Jouvenal, Helmer, Kahn, and Wiener) makes several assumptions about the future environment that reflect the work of the systems designers. It assumes that through policies of government and business, the work of constructing the environment *whole* in the future is not only possible but plausible; that futurist speculation and design must follow a systems approach; that no single technology or social structure can be separated from its future context; and finally, that planning for thirty years ahead is as necessary for the survival of large organizations as planning for the next fiscal year. If the systems engineers are reconstructing our ecology, the futurists are giving them the initial line drawings for their blueprints.

Critics of the futurists have accused them of dubious propheteering and a biased, technologically absorbed approach to emerging problems. Yet it seems that their two greatest shortcomings are that they limit their studies to national and international (rather than global) patterns, and that they do not sufficiently consider what Mumford calls "the cultural context."

Fred Polak's *The Image of the Future* provides a useful perspective on the futurists, for it shows historically the role that the future played in previous societies, whose institutions each contained its distinct utopian hope. Whether in this world or beyond it, hope has always been the most negotiable currency for politicians, clergy, academics, and merchants in dealing with society at large. The psychology of expectations, so important in any industrialized nation, plays no real role in the works of futurist systems designers like de Jouvenal, Helmer, Kahn, and Wiener.

Two treatments that do take expectations into account, as well as the importance of grappling with ecological patterns larger than national boundaries, are C. C. Furnas's *The Next One Hundred Years,* and John McHale's *The Future of the Future*. Furnas wrote in 1936, but his predictions retain their worth; many of them have already become fact. McHale, a collaborator of Buckminster Fuller, has introduced a fresh conception of future study by emphasizing the relationship between new technologies and world-wide ecological patterns. He suggests, for example, that the use of satellites will not only "speed up" the whole communications process, but likewise will obliterate the concept of distance as we know it in this context.

As design increasingly circumscribes and delineates the future, the concerns already raised in this book—the limits of change, the deterministic character of a technological environment, the precise relationships between people and their technology—promise to become even more problematical. What the systems designers and engineers herald—a world planned, organized, and conceived almost as a new technological utopia—seem more imminent than ever before. The misgivings of Mumford and the critique of Ellul about the gilded promise of technology seem more relevant here than anywhere else. Is a new utopia possible, or will the systems woven throughout man's experiences and institutions serve only to further constrain him?

AN ECOLOGY OF INFORMATION: NORBERT WIENER

The systems engineers hold out the promise of reconstructing the environment of the future in drastic, comprehensive ways. They will be assisted, in almost every venture, by that Pythagoras of the modern age, the computer. Indeed, one must look to the computer as much as the systems designers to glimpse some shape of the world as it is being reconstructed even today.

Although Norbert Wiener was historically related to the computer in much the same tangential way as the systems designers, his name has come to be associated with it. Wiener, a mathematician, has developed a theory of information by which man could interact more effectively with the computer. The term he coined for his theory, cybernetics, comes from the Greek word *kubernetes*: steersman. What Wiener struggled to reach, both in the matmematical and in the larger social realms, was a model for successful movement and control of information between man and machine. He was not interested only in the microcosm of an industry in which computers might become central to the management and organization. What fascinated and sometimes frightened him were the problems emerging from the central position of the computer in society at large: when men would depend upon computers and the information flowing between themselves and computers for maintaining political, economic, and cultural stability.

Wiener's theory of information control was developed by him and several other theorists—most notably W. Ross Ashby, John von Neumann, Claude Shannon, and Warren Weaver—during the late Forties. In 1948 Wiener published his book *Cybernetics* that developed his mathematical theory and made him the father of a new model of systems organization.

The book that has made Wiener an important figure in

interpreting the coming implications of the computer, however, was a brief series of essays published in 1950 with the striking title *The Human Use of Human Beings*. The man one discovers within this book is more than a mathematician: he comes across as a concerned social theorist examining the consequences of a science he had helped initiate. Social critics who claim that scientists ignore the larger social dimensions of their work cannot begin to fault Wiener; indeed, no one yet has shown as much perspicacity as Wiener in examining the various implications of the computer and the new routings of information that the computer creates.

Wiener derived much of the mathematical background in his development of cybernetics from the probability theories of Willard Gibbs. Gibbs, a mathematician, had devoted the brunt of his work to the problem of entropy, the tendency of any closed physical system to dissipate energy and run down. Because he dealt with gases and other materials that defied the traditional method of tracing an effect back to a single cause, Gibbs was forced to work in probabilities. If the temperature of a gas and the rate of its expansion are known, what are the other properties *most likely* to be? Wiener notes that this method differs significantly from that of Einstein and other major physicists who were "still talking primarily in terms of an absolutely rigid dynamics not introducing the idea of probability." Yet, Wiener notes, both Gibbs's probabilistic theories and Einstein's relativity "represent a shift in the point of view of physics in which the world as it actually exists is replaced in some sense or other by the world as it happens to be observed, and the old naive realism of physics gives way to something on which Bishop Berkeley might have smiled with pleasure."

Wiener applied Gibbs's work to information by observing that in any information system—whether a telephone circuit or an automated factory—the same tendency for entropy exists. Indeed, Wiener's concept of the universe is that of a highly organized system gradually deteriorating into a general, undifferentiated system in which change becomes increasingly unlikely. It is against this notion that he sees the importance of information movement and control, or cybernetics. Man, Wiener states, is a pocket of decreasing entropy in a universe of increasing entropy. This characteristic is shared by the computer, and to some extent by any communication system. What is needed is a method of routing information through the necessary channels to maintain stability or homeostasis of an organization, a system, a society, without the usual encroachments of entropy. Cybernetics supplies a model of that method.

A critical term in cybernetics is feedback, the ability of information to come full circuit and provide a means of autonomous control. A primitive example of feedback can be seen in a thermostat, which measures gradients in the temperature and sends messages back to the heating or cooling unit. Wiener describes feedback services in terms of sensors, monitors, and performance level—terms that apply equally to man and machine. Indeed, a major thrust in cybernetics lies in locating the common denominators between man and machine—how both can be controlled within a single system.

In Darwin's evolutionary theory organisms tend both toward a multi-directional (or experimental) pattern, and toward following the pattern of their ancestors. This combination resulted in Darwin's process of natural selection: the organisms best fitted (both by multi-directional or ancestral traits) to the new circumstances survive. Darwin comments that this "residual pattern" of natural selection *appears* as a kind of universal purposiveness. With Samuel Butler's *Erewhon* echoing in the background, Wiener shows how the learning process in machines follows an analogous route, leading again to the residual pattern, which takes on a tentative appearance of purposiveness. "Not only," comments Wiener, "can we build purpose into machines, but in an overwhelming majority of cases a machine designed to avoid certain pitfalls of breakdown will look for purposes which it can fulfill."

Unlike the human brain, a computer does not *remember* information, but has recourse to "memory banks" or taped information. When Wiener says of computers, "there is no reason why they may not resemble human beings in representing pockets of decreasing entropy in a framework in which the larger entropy tends to increase," he is not identifying computers with people, but searching out the mathematical point of basic equivalence between the two. There is an enormous difference between saying that a computer is like a man and saying that within a certain system of communication, the behavior of both man and machines can be similarly controlled by the same variables.

Cybernetics, then, comprises both the model of a system in which information can move harmoniously and guarantee equilibrium, and a further exploration of the implications and variables stemming from this model. In the period when he wrote the two books, Wiener looked to cybernetics as a means of providing the social and biological sciences with a fresh mathematical framework for a systems approach. The cybernetic method that had worked so well in physics and communication sciences could, he thought, apply equally well to other sciences. Generally it did not. As Jarislov Bronowski observed in 1964, shortly after Wiener's death, ". . . the heroic dream is over. Cybernetics remains in the best sense a fundamental idea as well as a popular one, but it has turned out to be less embracing and, in an odd way, less interesting than we had hoped 20 years ago when it was conceived."

It seems curious and slightly ironic that Wiener's book, *The Human Use of Human Beings,* would outlast in significance the science that it explained and interpreted. For the book has become something of a classic among systems designers, mathematicians, and men working in various fields relating them to the computer and systems approaches. And one suspects, or more pointedly, hopes, that it has reached this stature less for its explication of cybernetic theory than for its incisive and striking insights about the social and moral implications of the computer for society.

Wiener considers the introduction of the computer into society a process at once required by the demands and speed of society and yet precarious in its possible outcome. He does not seem to fear a vague dehumanization as much as an inability to maintain a conceptual, and implicitly moral and social, control over the machine. He seems to suggest that if we let the computer define its own territory, and apply its advantages to new areas without first analyzing the more likely consequences, we may witness a series of capitulations of man to the machine that far outscale anything previously suggested by history.

In one instance Wiener speculates that our relationship to the computer may grow into something quite similar to that between the Roman slaveholder and his Greek slave. The slaveholder is in a contradictory position: he wants his slave to be intelligent, but he also wants him to be subservient. As Wiener shrewdly remarks, "Complete subservience and complete intelligence do not go together. How often in ancient times the clever Greek philosopher slave of a less intelligent Roman slaveholder must have dominated the actions of his master rather than obeyed his wishes."

In another context, Wiener speaks even more grimly, referring obliquely to W. W. Jacobs's grisly story "The Monkey's Paw." In the story a family entrusts to the magic paw of a dead monkey the means of gaining a quick and easy hundred pounds—and finds that the cost is their son's life. The machine, writes Wiener, "which can learn and can make decisions on the basis of its learning, will in no way be obliged to make such decisions as we should have made, or will be acceptable to us. For the man who is not aware of this, to throw the problem of his responsibility to the machine, whether it can learn or not, is to cast his responsibility to the winds, and to find it coming back seated on the whirlwind."

The fears are real and urgent. They are not rooted in the spectre of Frankenstein's monster, as Ellul's tend to be, but more in the suggestion of Samuel Butler, that we are preparing the machine to better cope with the changing environment than man. The machine, as Butler insinuated, may yet take the thrust of evolution from man. Wiener not only concedes this as a scientific possibility, but considers it a likely consequence of man's failure to resist the encroachments on his freedom and responsibility that the machine represents.

TEN

Leapfrogging the Twentieth Century

R. BUCKMINSTER FULLER

I was born cross-eyed. Not until I was four years old was it discovered that this was caused by my being abnormally far-sighted. My vision was thereafter fully corrected with lenses. Until four, I could see only large patterns, houses, trees, outlines of people with blurred coloring. While I saw two dark areas on human faces, I did not see a human eye or a teardrop or a human hair until I was four. Despite my new ability to apprehend details, my childhood's spontaneous dependence only upon big pattern clues has persisted.

Buckminster Fuller

Richard Buckminster Fuller is a nineteenth-century inventor with twenty-first-century ideas. The fact that he lives in the twentieth century seems a dual anachronism. A hundred years ago he probably would have beaten Edison to the electric light—only calling it the "key to the pattern transformation of energy circuits," and using it as the springboard for expansive, grandiose ideas on man and technology. A century in the future he would be superb, heading the scientific oligarchy that controls the movement of solar resources. Nitrogen from Venus to the moon; ammonia from the moons to Saturn to Mars. No population, at whatever reach of Malthus's fears, would dint Fuller's passion for feeding, clothing, and sheltering everyone.

Fuller is a short, squat man, bald except for a thin, almost invisible patch of white hair—the archetype of the New England inventor. His life story, a rocky and for anyone but Fuller a depressing saga of bumping into closed doors and fixed ideas, flies full in the face of twentieth-century organizational ideals. Fuller is closer to Emerson than to the anonymous inventors in the laboratories of General Electric and I.B.M. He speaks and writes in a dialect of latinisms all his own. But nowhere else is his nineteenth-century character as manifest as in his unflagging belief that utopia is man's only alternative at this stage of his development. This trait is deeply rooted in the vision of the American utopians, from the founders of Brook Farm to Edward Bellamy. But it also draws its thrust from the energy sources of a post-Einstein civilization—from inventories of resource's transportation facilities, and geographical and ecological patterns. It is a utopia of the post-atomic engineer.

If Fuller's style harks back to the nineteenth century, the scale and effrontery of his ideas suggest the twenty-first. Fuller is an adamant futurist, concerned primarily with alternate possible human ecosystems rather than the narrow dangers and confines of the present situation. Compared with more exacting futurists like Daniel Bell, Herman Kahn, and Bertrand de Jouvenal, he seems rough-edged and erratic. Yet his central ideas hint that while the other futurists are drafting blueprints for the future, Fuller is blithely watching full-scale models whizz through his own elaborate mental version of the universe. Fuller thinks big.

Long before NASA launched men to the moon, Fuller was pressing his concept "spaceship earth" beyond analogy. The earth is a life-support system, he emphasizes, speeding through the universe at 125,000 miles per hour—not the "all" or "world," but merely humanity's temporary environment. Man's responsibility lies in making the most of that environment: letting it work in the best way for him, drawing upon it with respect for its possibilities and limitations. Men in a spaceship are not locked in one place, but become perpetual travelers. Fuller's vision of history is a cosmic odyssey of man, energy, and the hidden patterns and "event constellations" that he calls the universe.

Even more than most of the other men featured in this book, Fuller resists labels and categories. His work has ranged from architectural design to the invention of a new automobile, from radicalized geometry to metaphysics, from poetry (he calls it "ventilated prose") to ecological theory. Fuller darts between disciplines, propelled only by the conviction that we have long been missing many of the secret patterns underlying evolution and nature. Says Fuller of his own work, "I am not a creator. I am a swimmer and a dismisser of irrelevancies. Everything we need to work with is already around us, although most of it is initially confusing. To find order in what we experience we must first inventory the total experiences, then temporarily set aside all irrelevancies. I do not invent my thoughts. I merely separate out some local patterns from a confusing whole." Then, with typical aplomb, he points laconically to the advantage of his approach: "Flight was the discovery of the lift—not the push."

Russell Davenport, a friend and collaborator of Fuller's, has described him as "an architect of things in motion." Fuller's thought assumes a primacy of energy over fixed forms, of wholes over their parts. An important aspect of Fuller's work is his attempt to pioneer a new conceptualization of experience after Einstein—in much the same way as Milic Čapek and Korzybski have done. Fuller's first book, *Nine Chains to the Moon,* was a popularization of Einstein's theories. By 1938 Fuller was already postulating the range of transformations that modern physics would effect—in housing, in transportation, in commerce and geography. Throughout this book, as in his later writings and speeches, motion is the only constant. $E = mc^2$ is Fuller's key to a fresh, unique grasp of human ecology.

Fuller is best known as a designer of unusual but light and sturdy architectural forms. Thousands of his geodesic domes dot the globe. One of his latest (if for many critics, most preposterous) ideas, "tetra city," has been given serious consideration by Tokyo city planners. Tetra city is a megalithic pyramid, over a mile wide at the base and six hundred feet tall. It can float on water and contain up to a million inhabitants. Tetra city will probably not be built in this century, nor are geodesic forms likely to become commonplace within the next thirty years. Yet who can tell of the next century, when the housing and spatial demands that Fuller already recognizes become widely acknowledged?

Fuller's background is auspicious in its lack of academic signposts and for its variety of experiences. Born in 1895 in Milton, Massachusetts, he became the fifth generation of Harvard men in a proud lineage that included Rev. Timothy Fuller, a Massachusetts delegate to the Constitutional Convention, and Arthur Buckminster Fuller, a stalwart abolitionist. His grandmother, Margaret Fuller, was a leading spirit of Brook Farm and co-founder and editor of *The Dial*. In a family of individualists, Bucky proved himself to be more individualistic than most; he was expelled from Harvard twice and never returned to receive a degree.

During World War I, Fuller worked as an officer in the Navy, where he developed a combination mast, boom, and grappling hook to rescue seaplanes from rough waters. Later, he studied briefly at the U.S. Naval Academy at Annapolis, finding in the design requirements of ships a much more satisfying form of study than his academic courses at Harvard.

After the War, Fuller worked for his father-in-law in a firm that built construction materials. The clash between the weighty, archaic methods of house building and Fuller's background in ship design led him to the gradual recognition that new patterns for life-support systems, or what he later called "livingry," were needed. By 1927, a harsh year for Fuller, he realized that his experiences provided him with the training ground for some extraordinary technical achievements. Most of Fuller's major ideas and the practical inventions that stem from them can be traced back to the thoughts he had that year.

Throughout the late Twenties and early Thirties, Fuller proved to be a brilliant if eccentric inventor. By 1928 he applied for a patent on his dymaxion house, a six-sided, pyramid-shaped dwelling built on a central mast and capable of mass production and delivery by helicopter. The house included a fully equipped bathroom that required no plumbing. Drawing on aviation design, Fuller in 1932 designed his dymaxion car, (devised from "dynamic" and "maximum"—a trademark word for Fuller's inventions) a streamlined vehicle shaped like a dolphin, which moved on a totally rotational wheelbase. Although the car consumed less than half the fuel of standard automobiles for even better performance, a fatal and highly publicized accident in 1934 (for which the other car was later proved responsible) ruined its commercial possibilities.

During the late Thirties, Fuller was employed by the Phelps-Dodge Corporation, then as a technical consultant on the staff of *Fortune*. Working for the government during World War II, Fuller developed the first of his geodesic models, later to become his trademark "domes." Throughout the 1950s the domes became increasingly popular, and in the following decade Ford, Alcoa, and the American Pavilion at Montreal's Expo 67 had all proved the spatial worth of Fuller's design.

Fuller is often asked which came first, the designs or the

ideas—metaphysical, geographical, ecological—that they incorporate. Fuller claims that the inventions are simply offshoots of the ideas that have been developed in a number of singular, if somewhat erratic and stylistically florid, books. His *Untitled Epic Poem on the History of Civilization* was written in 1940, on the eve of war. The poem, which like much of Fuller's work has become popular only in the late 1960s, seems less like poetry than a scientific credo: Fuller's avowal of hope in man, in science, and in technology. Another poetic statement, *No More Secondhand God* was written shortly afterward, during the war. Fuller's most comprehensive book, *Ideas and Integrities* (1963), is subtitled "A Spontaneous Autobiographical Disclosure." It traces his background and learning experiences and shows how these have propelled him toward the development of his unique ideas. Several books by Fuller have appeared since: *Education Automation* (1963), Fuller's suggestions for a new framework of education; *Operating Manual for Spaceship Earth* (1969), a fresh statement of his main themes; *Utopia or Oblivion?* (1970), a collection of articles and addresses; and *I Seem to Be a Verb,* a collaboration with Quentin Fiore and Jerome Angle (*The Medium Is the Message*).

Between 1965 and 1968 Buckminster Fuller and John McHale developed a series of documents entitled "World Design Science Decade, 1965-1975," an inventory of world resources and the means by which these resources could be made available to the world's population by 1975. The six documents in this series are especially valuable for the penetrating way in which Fuller makes use of statistics.

Fuller's writing style is no public relations coup. It is a dense, almost impenetrable jungle of latinisms, labyrinthine sentence structures, and computer jargon. He defines universe, for example, as "the aggregate of all of humanity's consciously-apprehended and communicated experience with the nonsimultaneous, nonidentical, and only partially overlapping, always complimentary, weighable and unweighable, ever omni-transforming, event sequences." Norman Mailer has said of the astronauts that, befitting the heroes of a new age, they speak a new language, and can converse more comfortably with computers than with mere mortals. Fuller, the reader suspects, can converse more comfortably with himself or his growing coterie of protégés and similarly comprehensive-minded designers for whom such argot is the essence of the new communication.

One must approach Fuller's ideas much like a tour through a geodesic dome, glimpsing the whole structure at first from a distance, then at closer range noting the stresses and pattern that give shape to the whole. Precise relationships between ideas do not matter as much as the structural nature of those relationships. And in both his theories and his designs, these relationships are thoroughly synergetic.

Synergy is a familiar Fuller term, which he defines as "behaviors of whole systems unpredicted by the behavior of any of their parts." In a synergetic universe, two plus two equals five. Chrome nickel steel, for example, can bear almost one and a half times the pressure of the sum of the tensile strengths of its component metals. As with most compounds or alloys, chrome nickel steel acts synergetically.

Synergy characterizes Fuller's thought, constantly bringing two ideas together that result in a third, often unpredicted, idea. This method makes it hard to find "starting points" in Fuller's thought. It is more fruitful to focus on the way his ideas interact: how themes such as energy, resources, technology, evolution, ecology, geography, geometry and wealth interconnect and channel into one another. Synergy is not only Fuller's slide rule for interpreting the universe; it is the reader's slide rule for interpreting Fuller.

OUTSCALING UTOPIA

"If you are in a shipwreck," Fuller writes, "and all the boats are gone, a piano top buoyant enough to keep you afloat that comes along makes a fortuitous life preserver. But this is not to say that the best way to design a life preserver is in the form of a piano top. I think that we are clinging to a great many piano tops in accepting yesterday's fortuitous contrivings as constituting the only means for solving a given problem."

If most utopians have some easy way of relegating the institutions of the past to the junkyard of futility, few can compete with Fuller's piano top as a quick way of scrapping institutions that range from politics to house building. Fuller's utopia, reflecting his passion for utilizing all potential resources in the most economical way, regards political problems and ideologies as hardly necessary in the future for more than minor jobs of housekeeping. Fuller suggests that the alternative world he proposes in his "comprehensive anticipatory design science" should be wholly accomplished, or not attempted at all. But he differs from the classic utopians when he insists that utopia has become our only realistic alternative. The world, he says, has become too dangerous for anything less.

Fuller calls his comprehensive anticipatory design science the "metaphysical mastering of the physical." It is not enough simply to locate the patterns of energy in the world and the universe, he insists. They must be related in the most effective way to provide for the basic needs of the whole population. He has created a complex, elaborate game called "Making the World Work." Players must reorganize routes of distribution, extend new farming techniques, locate and utilize world resources in such a way that the resources become available to everyone.

The world game vividly reflects Fuller's ultimate concerns and ideas. The game is not competitive but collaborative: a reflection of Fuller's conviction that only by scrapping the individualistic and competitive behavior of the past can we begin to construct a truly successful world. More important, the game forces the players to think out the future and to do it whole. Nations give way to patterns of world trade. Local problems disappear in the fact of global crises. Difficulties are anticipated rather than dealt with once they emerge. In short, the game reflects Buckminster Fuller's most abiding effort: a comprehensive anticipatory design science.

In comprehensive anticipatory design science, the tricky word is "design." The function of design, Fuller notes, is to draw the most advantageous use from resources and energy patterns. Instead of building a freeway through the middle of a congested city, for example, a new city should be designed within an area where the geographical and resource factors make it self-supporting. True design, Fuller insists, must be comprehensive. It demands a knowledge of all major patterns in the universe, all energy systems, the pathways of present geography and human ecology. In the days of sailing ships, he points out, the great sea voyagers had to know the capacities of their ships, the shifting demands of ocean navigation and exploration techniques. They had to have the ability to maintain firm authority. They knew the earth instinctively as a whole. In their minds they organized the relationships between oceans and land masses far more effectively (meaning with more ecological accuracy) than the static, distorted maps. These were the early great designers, who created not only better and faster ships, but new routes across the world. Fuller looks to them as models because the range of their thinking was global.

A comprehensive anticipatory design science implies that man determines his own evolution. Fuller notes that in 1900 only one percent of the world's population was participating in the interacting wealth of the technologies then available; in

1914, six percent; in 1940, twenty percent; by 1960, forty-four percent. Theoretically, if the trend continued, the world's total population would eventually share the full benefits of industrialization. Yet Fuller fears that such "livingry"—the technologies, or wealth, by which men can live more successfully—might only come about in the future as a result of another bout of "killingry" (war and warfare technologies); historically, that has been the dominant ratio.

Fuller's design science assumes far more than he himself acknowledges. Although he frequently assails politicians and ideologies, he says little about alternatives to the present strife created by nationalism, usurpation of wealth, and ideological conflict. All the classical utopians assumed that in the ordered environment they prescribed, people would change for the better, and that greed, ambition, individualism, and other hindrances to a better society would dissolve in a harmony of wills. Fuller makes the same precipitous assumption, and his criticism of national boundaries, politicians, and ideologies suffers from that naïveté. Politics may indeed be obsolete from the viewpoint of potential technologies and resources as Fuller believes; but men in power and national pride will not go away because people are no longer hungry.

Fuller's economy of wealth, similar to those popularized by John Kenneth Galbraith, Robert Theobald, and Barbara Ward, assumes that economic demands should take precedence over political mindsets. "The primacy of political ideologies is obsolete because they were all developed on the basis of the exclusive survival only of your party or my party—simply because there was not enough for both." Politicians, for Fuller, assume that there is just so much wealth in the world, and the one who can fight the hardest gets the most. Fuller argues that this is not the case; wealth multiplies as technologies make the process of extricating products and energies increasingly easier. Fuller's principle of "ephemeralization," or more-from-less, operates at the center of technological evolution. A quarter-ton communications satellite can do more work than 150,000 tons of transoceanic cable. Wealth is not derived from money or even from pre-industrial forms of wealth. It comes from ever-expanding technological capacities. The politicians don't understand this, and they impede the progress of global design by insisting that wealth be hoarded and controlled, rather than contributed to the evolving process of technology.

Suppose, asks Fuller, a comprehensive anticipatory design science were implemented on a global scale. The waves of that revolution would submerge politics and ideologies forever. Any new era must discard the obsolete tools that helped shape it, but that now hinder its progress. For Fuller the politicians represent the descendants of the great pirates—the sea venturers who turned their genius for design into conquest and booty. Although politicians and their ideologies were needed to catalyze its early growth, industry reaches a threshold (and on a world scale has already reached it) where these forces become redundant—huge megaliths obstructing the throughways of the future.

Politicians are not the only obstacle to a global design science. We continue clinging to fixed places, when in reality these no longer exist for most of us. Most New Yorkers, he says, "still think of *permanence as normal,* a hangover from the Newtonian view of the universe. But those who have lived in and with New York since the beginning of this century have literally experienced living with Einsteinian relativity." Permanence is no more than an illusion, as unyielding as a woman's weekly hairdo. "New York's permanent-wave architecture is in fact a progressively rippling dynamic wave system. The last half-century has seen three successive replacements of would-be permanent New York buildings." Even the population is anything but permanent, Fuller claims; the average residence in the city is three years. Despite these facts, many New Yorkers continue to orient themselves geographically, politically, and economically on the basis of a static image of the city that exists in their minds.

The illusion of permanence makes the work of convincing people of the need for global design doubly difficult. "Lacking dynamic apprehension it is difficult for humanity to get out of its static fixations and specifically to see great trends evolving." No matter to what extent mobility has replaced permanence, Fuller argues, people still think of mobility as the exception, rather than the rule.

Comprehensive anticipatory design reflects both Fuller's careful scientific grounding and his utopian imagination. By insisting on the need for design, Fuller suggests that the routes of change can be mapped, and indeed should be. He admits that much of the progress already made toward world industrialization and a global ecology was begun without the aid of conscious planning; yet such trends must be met in the future with the collaboration of designers. The problem with most previous designs for improving society, including those of the systems designers, is that they have been too narrow in gauging available resources, too shortsighted. Whatever the limitations and eccentricities of Fuller's theories, no one can accuse him of thinking too small.

OLD ENERGIES AND NEW SYNERGIES

Fuller interprets the major environments as forms of energy, and not primarily as the content of the human sensorium. Indeed, he argues that the sensory range has been virtually abolished: the new sciences of the twentieth century require instruments to measure what the senses cannot, for the environmental energies with which they deal lie beyond man's perceptual range.

Where Wiener's is an ecology of information, Fuller's is an ecology of mobility patterns, the ways in which men and commodities move. When Fuller designs a new geodesic dome, he is as concerned with getting the construction materials to the site as he is with making sure they are light, well-fitted, durable. Mobility patterns provide Fuller with clues to the whole range of human ecology, and he depends upon those clues more than any other factor, seeking out what is most advantageous and economical.

Man's evolution is a function of shifts in his ecology. Fuller calls it "ecological pattern transformation." When eels, plovers, and other biological species were forced to alter their developed ecological patterns, they did it unconsciously. Man's process of adapting to and transforming a new environment is a conscious one, signifying a new stage in biological evolution.

Fuller sees the most recent major ecological pattern transformation in the revolution achieved by the automobile and the airplane. His father spent most of his life within a twenty-four-mile radius of his home (the average visual distance to the horizon), and traveled—by foot and vehicle—little over sixteen hundred miles a year. Fuller himself often sweeps across the globe on a daily basis, averaging over 100,000 miles a year. Man has stepped from a localized community into a world community.

Man's present ecology reveals a pattern of mobility so pronounced in its latitude and its thrust that institutions from banking to national politics are cast into unacknowledged obsolescence. Fuller foresees that the rate of mobility will continue to spiral. Even the cities, viewed presently as the congested victims of our increasing mobility, will prove in the future to be no more than "a present way station phase of man's increasing deployment pattern."

Fuller's ecological concept of evolution resembles Julian Huxley's "social evolution" and Teilhard de Chardin's "noosphere." All three suggest that man can consciously pattern his own evolution, and that technology represents the new nerve fibers of an emerging super-organism. This latter emphasis is especially strong in Fuller.

Fuller was one of the first to call serious attention to tools as extensions of man and industry as an extension of society. One of Fuller's prime tenets is the uninterrupted flow of the same patterns and energy forms between man and the universe. For him, man and universe interact as complementary parts of a whole process, and this process is inseparable from man himself. Fuller sees no barrier and no distinction between the "microcosm" and "macrocosm," terms that have evolved from a period of anthropocentrism. Now that new instruments can extend man's sensory range, he becomes part of a continuous, enlarging pattern, and man's consciousness of this fact must guide his ideas about himself and his world.

Fuller roots his principle of organic continuity in the consistency of structures. The same principles that give his geodesic domes their strength and tensional force are operative in an eggshell or an algae cell. Since so few people are aware of this inner consistency in nature (a consistency that is to be found as well in technology), Fuller suggests we have many wrongheaded ideas about the nature of man's relationship to the world. "Even today, despite interim development of fundamental knowledge to the contrary, we speak erroneously of 'artificial' materials, 'synthetics,' and so forth. The basis for this erroneous terminology is the notion that Nature has certain things which we call natural, and everything else is 'man made,' *ergo* artificial. But what one learns in chemistry is that Nature wrote all the rules for structuring; man does not invent chemical structuring rules; he only discovers the rules.

All the chemist can do is to find out what Nature permits, and any substances that are thus developed or discovered are inherently *natural*."

Design science is not a science of invention, but of discovery and collaboration. Four basic tenets of the Fuller philosophy reflect this: the dymaxion principle; ephemeralization; fluid geography; and Fuller's theory of tools and industry.

Fuller's early designs in automobiles, housing, and maps have been called dymaxion—a combination of "dynamic" and "maximum." The principle underlying a dymaxion structure is its ability to draw the greatest possible performance out of each unit of input on the basis of available technologies. The term is primarily descriptive, but instructive as well. A dymaxion house is not only a living unit, but the most economical living unit possible.

Dymaxion inventions result from the principle of ephemeralization, which is one of the primary thrusts of technology. It means more work with less energy, more competence with less manpower, more total productivity with less specialization. Ephemeralization works at all levels of an industrial system—from the design of instruments to what Fuller calls the total "energy-wealth system." Communications satellites are already replacing transoceanic cables; eventually the satellites will themselves be far simpler and less costly laser beams. Fuller is particularly optimistic about the industrialized world, largely because of the inherent operation of ephemeralization. "The larger the energy-wealth system, the more efficiently does it operate. Conversely, as energy systems grow larger they lose energy more slowly."

If movement patterns are the key to Fuller's ecology, then his "fluid geography" is the master blueprint of potential movement patterns. The geography he has developed is scaled to the interrelations between land and water masses. The dymaxion map, one of the outgrowths of his fluid geography, reflects Fuller's attempt to devise a global, energy-oriented conception of geography.

Fuller's dymaxion map presents an image of the globe that, while flat, can easily be converted into a near-spherical, three-dimensional shape. None of the land masses have been amputated, and the whole of the earth's surface is presented with an accurate ratio of water to land. The significant feature of the dymaxion map, however, is the viewpoint it provides toward the arrangement of land masses and seas. The world as viewed from this map is something of a continuous movement of land over the Arctic Circle, interconnected on the sides by waters of varying dimensions. The map recommends the use of water rather than land for major movements. It relates land and water in a unique way, suggesting that the land is closed, the waters are open. In effect, it contributes toward an image of the world that is more fluid than terrestrial, more energetic than fixed.

The dymaxion principle, ephemeralization, and fluid geography suggest the dynamic character of Fuller's ecology. Perhaps nowhere else, however, is this as evident as in Fuller's theory of industry which Fuller defines as the "integrated, teleologic objectivity of the full gamut of the exact sciences." "Teleologic"—a rare word in a scientist's vocabulary—suggests two features in industry: its constant self-regeneration and its orientation to a purpose—both the immediate purpose of a product, and the larger purpose of contributing to a total design. No single technology, therefore, is autonomous; if industry is man's external organism, its total complex is society's external shape.

The basis of technology is tools. Fuller distinguishes between craft tools and industrial tools. Craft tools, he states, are those "which can be spontaneously fashioned and adopted by any one individual starting nakedly in the wilderness—for instance, his picking up a stone to do work at a distance greater than arm's length." Industrial tools, however, are those that cannot be produced by any one man. Craft tools are autonomous and static; industrial tools are interconnected and can regenerate themselves. Moreover, they tend to contribute toward the more complex development of their own kind. For example, language, the first industrial tool, became the prerequisite for all the industrial tools to follow.

Throughout history, especially recent history, the development of industrial tools has depended significantly upon what Fuller calls "killingry"—the sciences and technologies propelled by war. World War I made far more refrigerators available afterward than would have been the case without a war, because the war both accelerated the industrial process and forced new methods of engineering refrigeration motors. Fuller considers this translation from killingry to livingry as part of the evolutionary process of industry, or what he calls "the industrial equation." The intrusion of atomic weapons does not necessarily change the industrial equation, though it does darken the chances for continuing the killingry-livingry transition on its earlier basis.

The industrial process alters the physical environment permanently, and man temporarily. On one level, it evolves constantly toward an ever-increasing elimination of man from physical and specialist tasks. Likewise, it tends to expand the boundaries of any industry beyond the familiar national or geographical borders. Fuller counters the claims of skeptics who feel that we are fast depleting our resources; rather, he insists, the junkyard becomes the new lode mine. "With today's impounding of total resources through the progressive recycling and re-conversion of inventory materials, science has hooked up the everyday plumbing to the cosmic reservoir."

The specific relationship between man and his technologies lies at the heart of Fuller's theory of evolution. Man has reached a threshold of evolution where the organic changes become transferred to the environment, so that rather than altering the shape of his hand or the accuracy of his eye organically, man hastens his evolution by extending his hand or his eye through tools and instruments. The tension in evolution, and to a large extent in mankind of the twentieth century, lies in the "attempt by man to convert his evolution from a subjective to an objective process." There are enough mechanisms within the process of industry (ephemeralization, the dymaxion principle) to keep evolution from a collision course, but as the process speeds up—as it has so dramatically in this century—man is faced with the option of controlling his evolution consciously through design or permitting the old fixations of war, aggression, and individualism to clash with the new environment, creating almost unbearable stresses.

Man shapes his destiny by shaping his environment, and the process must now become conscious, global in scope, and totally anticipatory, if we hope to survive. Man has nothing to fear from technology; on the contrary, technology implicitly leads toward doing more with less. The problem lies in the belief that a newer and better civilization can be built on the piano tops that bob so precariously in the turbulent change of our time.

WILL THE HOUSE OF THE FUTURE BE A HOUSE?

Houses are in many ways man's most common and unnoticed environments. We consider them fixed in space, a principle of stasis in a whirlwind of change. Yet Fuller maintains that we are about to witness a revolution in housing that will change both attitudes and conceptions of what the house is, and what it is for. " 'House,' in comprehensive designing, would be as incidental to the world-around network dwelling service as is the telephone transceiver instrument to the energy processing in communication systems, which are in turn within the larger systems of industry." Houses of the present are the accretions of a long and hardly dynamic tradition of house-building. The house of the future will be scientifically constructed, a total dwelling unit offering the most advantages for the materials, weight, and energy that go into making it. Will it look like a house? Probably not. It may be a unit in "tetra city." It may be a free-floating geodesic sphere, moored temporarily like a houseboat in one place, then free to float the skies (these may be even more practical in moon colonization than in the earth's denser atmosphere). It may be a geodesic dome within larger, encompassing geodesic domes—the alternatives that Fuller presents have all the earmarks of bold but carefully researched science fiction. As nowhere else in his thought, Fuller's concepts of housing seem to belong totally in the twenty-first century.

Critics have long chided Fuller for his geodesic dome and other housing designs. A dome is the most uninteresting shape aesthetically. A suburbia of domes would appear more hideous and look-alike than anything presently inside or outside our cities. Such criticism is true, as far as it goes; but Fuller would hardly applaud the idea that domes become the new fixation of a patterned suburbia. Quite the contrary. A major benefit of comprehensive design is that it permits new arrangements, new possible integrations of housing units. Besides, the two central advantages of the dome are its spatial experience and its unique construction.

Spatially, a geodesic dome is far more fascinating and richer in possible individual alteration than the present house. Despite the influence of innovators like Louis Sullivan and Frank Lloyd Wright, most houses are designed on the two-dimensional model of a blueprint. Floors, walls, and ceilings meet in distinct rectangular fashion; there are no curves, no suggestions of space beyond walking one way or walking another. A geodesic dome contains far more ceiling, or "above-the-head" space than most traditional dwellings. Walls are not designed into the house, and therefore can be flexible and temporary. Japanese screens, for example, can serve as breakers between different "rooms," none of which need to exist if their function (such as a guest bedroom) ceases to exist. Geodesic domes are quite common in recent communes, and for good reason; besides being economical and sturdy, their spatial configuration encourages a tribal, rather than a specialized and segmented, mode of life.

Fuller did not design the geodesic domes for their unique spatial advantages as much as simply because such structures can enclose the greatest amount of space for the least amount of work the materials have to do. While working for his father-in-law's construction firm at the age of thirty, Fuller observed that the building industry continued to erect most of its structures on the sole principle of compression—an idea over four thousand years old. Brick upon brick may create an adequate dwelling, but hardly a scientifically economic one—in terms of what we know today about materials. It likewise seems foolish if there aren't enough bricks or skilled bricklayers to go around.

Fuller's architecture works basically on the principle of "tensional integrity" ("tensegrity," for short)—countering compression with tension, so that the interacting stress provides a solid frame. A simple example of tensegrity is a barrel. While a barrel's sides are compressed inward at the ends by the tines or hoops, their natural tendency is to spring back into their original flat shape. This creates a tension that fights the compression. The process of two counterforces gives the barrel a strength far greater than a box could ever possess.

Tensional integrity, Fuller claims, is the key principle underlying most natural and organic structures. The primary component of tensegrity structures is the triangle, and Fuller has shown how phenomena from DNA helixes to the cornea of the human eye all reveal a complex grouping of triangular stresses—producing the curvilinear structures that are the most stable form possible.

The principle of tensegrity forms the primary axiom of Fuller's "energetic-synergetic geometry," his unique mathematical system for dealing with energetics and closed spaces. As a schoolboy, Fuller found the tenets of Euclidean geometry abstract and meaningless. It seemed to be based on a view of the world as a flat, two-dimensional surface. Fuller admits that such a geometry might serve the basic compositional demands of a pre-Newtonian or Newtonian world, but we have learned too much recently that refutes such a "dead" geometry. Fuller developed energetic-synergetic geometry partly in defiance of Euclid, partly because of the needs for developing his own structures. Rather than a language of point, line, plane, Fuller's geometry employs a language of stress, tension, tensional integrity, vector equilibrium, octahedron, tetrahedron. Despite a proliferation of alternative geometric systems since Pascal and Descartes, Fuller insists that his is capable of relating totally to the changed conception of the universe since quantum physics.

Fuller does not contend that energetic-synergetic geometry is his own, but rather that it articulates patterns already inherent in nature. The arch of a leaf follows the same structural focus used in the building of a suspension bridge. The forces that guide the microcosm can be made to guide the macrocosm, and energetic-synergetic geometry is the key to those forces. As Fuller's biographer Robert Marks states, "The limits of the visible spectrum did not represent the threshold of change between man-devised structures and nature-devised structures. There was, in fact, no threshold."

Whenever Fuller speaks to a group of architectural students, he states that architects have focused too much on the subjective aspects of housing, and have almost totally neglected its objective side. Architecture should be a science, dominated from within by principles as ineluctable as those guiding physics or chemistry. Rather than think basically in terms of the sensory impact of form or texture before building a dwelling, architecture should think of the relative economy of building with lighter materials, using dynamic principles rather than a sole dependence on weight and compression. Once, speaking to a group at Northwestern University, he opened the lecture with a question: "What do you think this building weighs?"

No longer can architects assume that a house is a house is a house. The automobile, Fuller notes, has already replaced the large porches that were a common feature of houses built before World War I. Today's present ecological patterns are moving at such a pace that soon the very concept of the house as a fixed entity may no longer have meaning. Yet present architectural techniques demand that a house be thought of as a permanent, fixed part of the landscape.

Fuller admits that his own ideas will not prompt the much-needed revolution in housing, but that space exploration will. For at the heart of the effort to propel men to the stars lies the need to design for them comprehensive life-support systems on the most economic scale possible. What we learn from the first space journeys about the technological possibilities for improving livingry, Fuller assures, will be just as important as what we learn about the universe. Earth homes will be modeled one day on the space ship.

Housing in the future will tend to become invisible. Many of Fuller's domes, such as the American Pavilion at Expo 67 or Wood's Hole Restaurant in Massachusetts, have been enclosed in a skin of thin, clear plastic, creating the sense that only a latticework truss separates the inside from the outside. side.

Housing, Fuller insists, can no longer be left adequately to the tradition-locked patterns of individual architects and builders. A comprehensive anticipatory design science should organize and energize the building of new houses, as well as of new cities. The parts of houses could be produced tomorrow on an assembly-line basis, at far lower prices and with no real danger of losing the individuality possible through present construction methods. The famous Kaiser Dome in Honolulu was built in California, shipped to Hawaii, and constructed there in less than one day. It measures 150 feet in diameter.

The house of the future will not be a house, but part of a larger pattern of mobility and a global, communal involvement that we can barely glimpse at this time. If the city is, in Fuller's terms, merely "a present way station phase of man's increasing deployment pattern," then what of the house?

THE IMAGE IN THE GEODESIC DOME

It can be argued that, environmentally, a building is as important for what it reflects on the outside as for the life style it creates on the inside. Manhattan's skyscrapers invariably reflect other Manhattan skyscrapers. A clear geodesic dome reflects the onlooker and his vantage point. From wherever a person approaches a geodesic dome, he glimpses himself, distorted by the curved surface, but mirrored plainly against his background.

The difference is significant. In an organizational age, the towering flat-surfaced skyscrapers reflect what is most important in the culture: themselves. In another, post-organizational age, the reflection may once again become man and the whole landscape of earth—technological and natural.

Will it? The profound question raised by Fuller's theories, and possibly the ultimate criticism of them, is whether he promises a valid society for man or a crystalline technological dream—a geodesic eggshell containing a dead embryo.

What are Fuller's ultimate values, and how do these function in his comprehensively designed world? Fuller's poetry, as well as his other writings, reveal a significant bias. Words like "measurement," "weighable," "expansion," and "patternings" reappear with almost tiring frequency. They suggest that at the core of his thought is a quantitative standard for interpreting and judging phenomena. Even his pet concepts, synergy, ephemeralization, and energy are measurable and therefore quantitative entities. Fuller feels far more comfortable with quantitative standards and ideas than with purely qualitative ones. He believes in utopia because he can envision it quantitatively. There *is* enough food, he argues; the wealth is there for building the dwellings, the world can survive. Problems that involve qualitative analyses and decisions, such as politics or the mythic structure of nationalism, are brushed off in a metaphor about piano tops as life preservers.

One immediate result of Fuller's faith in quantities is his confidence in the computer. "A new, physically uncompromised, metaphysical initiative of unbiased integrity could unify the world," he writes. "It could and probably will be provided by the utterly impersonal problem solutions of the computers. Only to their superhuman range of calculative possibilities can and may all political, scientific, and religious leaders acquiesce." Fuller seems to be turning with bright hopes to the very possibilities that others, from Mumford through Wiener, have feared as the darkest of evils, man giving control of the planet over to the machine.

Fuller's quantitative bias does not negate his humanism (he *does* want to feed and shelter the whole race, and few have spoken out so consistently about the feasibility of doing so), but this bias seems subtly to undermine it. So you design a world society with comprehensive planning: is that a place for people to *live*? Jane Jacobs and others have shown that cities are delightful precisely because of their *unplanned* character

—the variety of experiences, the serendipity of a street where planning would have imposed a harsh uniformity. Comprehensive anticipatory design sounds fine before the fact; but people (and even computers) make mistakes, and who could anticipate the full flavor and needs of society in another era?

Fuller's suggestions that politics dissolve and that a world oligarchy of resource controls (he never explicitly mentions this, but that would seem to be the outcome) replace it contains all the makings for a very dictatorial utopia. There are some interesting relationships between Fuller and Marx that bear looking into. Both men constructed their utopian format largely out of a reaction to the technological developments of a major industrial era. Both assumed that the extant political framework could not relate to the coming needs of people. Both proposed a radical and totally designed alternative. Marx's alternative was rooted in economic theory and Hegel's interpretation of history. Fuller's alternative is rooted in quantum physics and industrial growth. Marx's ideas changed history only in the century after he lived and died. And who can say yet of Fuller?

Related to Fuller's quantitative bias is his deterministic theory of environments. Fuller believes that people can be changed when the environment changes. Here lies the essential progress of evolution, and this premise serves as the foundation-stone for his utopia. He fails to say exactly *how* environments change people, or in what ways, or to what extent. But one of his analogies suggests that there are virtually no limits. If a wasp flies into a house, he explains, it probably won't like being out of the sunshine, and will try to escape. But since it is unable to distinguish between open space and window glass, it keeps smashing futilely into the glass. In this sense it is a victim of its environment. Inside the house a woman, terrified by the wasp, tries to shoo it out with a rolled newspaper. This only further antagonizes the wasp, because its behavior pattern responds to light and darkness, not to a rolled-up newspaper. Rather than try to change the wasp's behavior, Fuller recommends, the woman should use the paper to cover the window. In other words, change the environment in such a way that it builds upon present behavior patterns and guides them. Fuller uses this analogy to show the futility of trying to change behavior directly. But it illustrates his assumption that human behavior is largely a function of the environment. The concept of behavioral control, espoused by B. F. Skinner and Thomas Watson (and, less noticably, by a generation of social scientists and systems designers), is not far afield from Fuller at all. The question arises whether, in a totally controlled environment, man continues to be free—or was that perhaps an illusion all along?

These are valid criticisms—so far as they go. They mark the boundaries of Fuller's genius, but do not discredit it. Fuller's accomplishments remain prodigious and, if only for their sheer originality, remarkable. Fuller has introduced drastic and needed ideas about housing, ecology, geography, design, geometry, technology, and the future. He has introduced a scale of thought that has already influenced a generation of architects and planners, and promises to influence future generations still further. Above all, perhaps, Fuller has shown that erratic and even nonspecialist genius can flower in the twentieth century. If Leonardo were alive today, he would probably have received the stymied response so familiar to Fuller.

The ultimate irony of Richard Buckminster Fuller is that for a man whose thought is so profoundly integral (indeed, for whom integrity is the first requisite of thought), the greatest danger seems to lie in accepting his ideas whole. As with McLuhan and Innis (the two men in this book closest to Fuller in the spirit of exploration), the whole is *not* always greater than the sum of its parts. Synergy, so revered by Fuller, fails him in the end. But perhaps he knew this all along. No one man can redesign the world alone, even with the help of nature's geodesic patterns. Buckminster Fuller has spent a lifetime playing gadfly to the twentieth century. Perhaps, a hundred years from now, the right pieces will fall into place, and the scale and originality of Fuller's thought might hallmark the efforts he has envisioned. One can only hope that it will not come too late, or come with the darker implications that Fuller has not foreseen.

ELEVEN

Beyond Technology

It is quite possible that the next great age of science will be dedicated not to the study of the "outer" world of nature, nor to the "inner" world of the psyche, but to an exhaustive examination of those processes that take place at the interface between the bilogical/neural imprints and the stimuli that constantly bombard them. . . . This new science—we might call it "the third science"—may come up with a working field theory of a man/world "hyphenation," just as our contemporary physics has expressed the equivalence of mass and energy and space/time and as psychology has come up with the mind/body concept. We are beginning to move into the world of hyphens; holes that may lead us to other spheres. We may find, in this third science we have postulated, that there is no meaningful distinction between the world and man, except as thinking makes it so.

Dan Fabun, *The Dynamics of Change*

If the appearance of men like Harold Innis, Marshall McLuhan, and Buckminster Fuller means anything in terms of our relationship to the technology we have created, it may be that the age of anthropocentrism is ended. We can no longer separate ourselves from our environment, nor—as Mumford and Ellul attempt—successfully oppose ourselves to it. Man exists as a part of and because of a larger context; and the central problem of our age is that the context springs increasingly out of man's spiraling knowledge.

The search for a principle of organic continuity between man and his technologies led Innis to a unique grasp of the role of media in history; McLuhan to a theory of perceptual ratios as the bearers of cultural change; Wiener to a science of communication between man and computers; and Fuller to the need for a global system design. In each case man and his environment become inseparable—interacting phases of a larger whole. Technology not only expands man's capacities, it expands man.

An organic continuity between man and his technologies is no guarantee of a prospective utopia, or even that new technologies bring improved conditions and better values. It does ensure against Mumford's pessimism that the machine is diametrically opposed to the organic. It likewise ensures against a total technological determinism as seen in Ellul, where man becomes totally enslaved to his creation.

The principle of organic continuity argues that the traditional means of understanding the impact of technology (upon institutions such as economics, politics, the city) defeat their purpose, for they presuppose that man and his institutions are only "affected" by the new environment. McLuhan has insisted that new environments reshape cultures whole; therefore, any exploration of environmental interaction will always start at a new place. And exploration is the method. No one, with the possible exception of Ellul, has proposed a system or a full-fledged interpretation of the new environments. Innis, McLuhan, and Fuller are particularly diffuse in their approach; their thought is scattered over a range of disciplines, and contradictions are not infrequent. Yet they insist that such forms of thought are demanded by the scale of the onslaught of change.

There are no single principles, no single methodologies or conclusions reached by the men in this book. They have done little more than to point ways, and these are divergent and often totally irreconcilable. Yet, combined, their thought comprises the most original and developed ideas toward an understanding of man's relationship to his spiraling technologies. They are a starting point, no more; but an impressive and highly advantageous starting point.

TWELVE POSTULATES

The ideas that emerge from the works of Mumford, Giedion, Ellul, Innis, McLuhan, Fuller, and the others mentioned in this volume can be crystallized into a set of postulates. It would be both premature and misleading to give these ideas the dogmatic weight of "principles" or "laws." They are closer to hypotheses—the provisional maps of the explorer rather than of the expert cartographer, for we are dealing with pathfinders, not sedate surveyors.

I have been able to identify twelve such postulates. The first three refer to the nature and scale of environmental analysis. The next three are propositions for the necessary method. The final six deal explicitly with the structures and evolution of technology.

TECHNOLOGY IS THE NEW METAPHYSICS. Ernst Jünger was the first to make the equation, but its implications abound in the works of these theorists. The ancient questions of duration and change, perception and reality, determinism and free will, time and space have taken on a new intensity and impetus in a technological age. In some instances (*viz.*, McLuhan updating Bergson) the questions have been modified. Yet they remain the ultimate questions posed in exploring the ultimate impact of new environments.

It is significant that these writers have arrived at the old questions through asking relatively new ones. Precisely how and to what extent does an environment reshape the culture?

Is the mechanical or electronic instrument to be *opposed* to organic man, or seen as an extension of him? Does technology evolve solely through the control and decisions of men or is it somehow (as Ellul and Fuller suggest) autonomous? The questions raised by these men are not academic in any sense of the word; they involve the moral furies of the epoch and reach a scale metaphysical in its proportions.

THINGS AREN'T WHAT THEY USED TO BE. Including words and their meanings. These thinkers are liberal with their vocabularies and freely expand a word to mean more than its original definition encompassed. Ellul's "technique" goes beyond technology into areas such as group dynamics and teaching methods. McLuhan's uses words such as "media," "environments," and "electronic" as probes to test the extremes of the environment. Fuller's language connotes the unfamiliar range and complexity of his thought.

These men are dealing with processes—complex movements that shun the effort of precise definition and welcome the experimental phrase, the overloaded word. Perhaps one might infer from Innis and Ellul that printed language is not the final medium for environmental thought; possibly the coming great thinkers in this field will express themselves best in film or recording. (Perhaps, no assuring thought, they already have.) The problem is one of maintaining the freedom to pursue new constructs of thought—constructs that traditional writing styles inhibit. To fault Innis, McLuhan, or Fuller for their "impossible" styles and overextended use of words is to miss their thrust toward radically new concepts and relationships.

ASSUMPTIONS AND ENVIRONMENTS ARE INVISIBLE. Virtually all the men in this volume have emphasized the invisible character of new environments. The tendency to see the old environment in the similarities of the new one is a common human problem of classification: whether in considering television as "movies at home" or the automobile as the "horseless carriage." Mumford refers to the "cultural pseudomorph"; Ellul emphasizes the ways in which technique has fostered its own invisibility; Innis points to the failure of established powers to react to a new and subversive medium until too late; a basic McLuhan axiom is that the old environment becomes the content of the new environment.

But the invisibility of major environments only serves to make these men aware of other invisible forms, namely assumptions—both their own and the common-sense assumptions toward the environment. McLuhan's preoccupation with perception is rooted in his conviction that preconceptions too often take the place of fresh perception. Ellul, Innis, and Fuller all reflect a serious attempt to override previous attitudes toward the ideas each of them deals with. "What is demanded," said Bertrand Russell, "is a change in our imaginative picture of the world." Most of these men can accept nothing less than a drastic new conceptualization of daily phenomena. Previous assumptions, however invisible, inhibit such a change.

EVIDENCE IS WHERE YOU FIND IT. If the major environments are invisible, how then can investigators support their interpretations of them? Boldly. Except for Mumford and Giedion, who deal with legitimate forms of historical data, these theorists use unorthodox and sometimes highly unusual means of gathering evidence. Innis supports his interpretation of history with the most minute and the most abstruse forms of data crowded side by side: one sentence might contain an obscure reference to an Alexandrian library as well as a sweeping judgment about medieval architecture, and within the framework of his thought, the two will support his thesis quite effectively. McLuhan's ubiquitous grasp of data is well-known; mesh stockings can be as valid and valuable for his argument as Shakespeare or Einstein. Fuller uses data, much of it statistical, for both rhetorical emphasis and measurement of the present validity of his thesis.

Such wayward uses of evidence would seem to undercut the efforts of these men, weaken and detract from their final theories. What these discrepancies reveal, however, is the heuristic nature of the effort. Ellul, Innis, McLuhan, and Fuller attempt less to prove than to postulate, suggest, and explore. Not working within an established discipline, they are not bound by the assumptions and methods of that discipline. They are free, in effect, to use whatever evidence they find, no matter where they find it.

HISTORY IS ANONYMOUS. Alexandria may have been named after Alexander the Great, but for Harold Innis its significance lay less in its great heroes and patriarchs than in its libraries and its grip on parchment deep into the Middle Ages. The idea that history is molded by environments rather than people was popular for a while in the nineteenth century (Burke and Burkhardt are two examples), but has lost much of its force recently. From Mumford to Innis, these men begin with the assumption the new technologies shape the contours of history, though not necessarily in their own likeness. Virtually all these men likewise assume that these changes did not come as a result of anyone's control—nor that controls are as easy to maintain as the systems designers might think.

THE DENIAL OF LOGIC. The methods of these theorists only rarely follow conventional paths of logic. Ellul's work shows the greatest use of it, but in the end even Ellul argues most cogently from insight and overstatement. Innis and McLuhan can be confounding; Fuller has discovered his own ornate, synergistic logic. Studying the interaction between men and their environments, these thinkers have been forced beyond the limits of logic into new systems and methods of their own. Freud certainly followed no conventional logic in deciphering the stratagems of the mind, and the same justification applies largely here. The bombardment of environments does not affect man through any logical sequence or in any presently measurable way. McLuhan has noted that logic and other icons of rationalism can obscure as much as they clarify. Perhaps the conscious refusal to follow conventional logic marks one of the most original and significant features of their thought.

TECHNOLOGY IS RADICALLY AMBIVALENT IN ITS EFFECTS. The idea pulses through Mumford, suggests itself in Ellul and Innis, undergirds Giedion and Wiener, receives some fascinating twists in McLuhan, and can be glimpsed in Fuller. Namely, the introduction of a new technology breeds effects that tend to be radically contradictory; and as technology evolves into further complexity, the opposition grows more and more extreme.

A simple example is Mumford's depiction of the steam engine in the nineteenth century. Its benefits were enormous: more power, more consumer goods, new networks of transportation, faster travel. But other consequences were grim: the oppression of the worker, especially the miner; the spread of vast urban slums where people lived on the edge of an animal existence; a new economic stranglehold by the capitalist investors.

Such an example is fairly self-evident. New technologies (or for that matter, any new, drastic changes in the structure of a society) have always tended to breed ambivalent effects. The real import of the principle of radical ambivalence lies in noting the tendency for new technologies to spiral toward increasingly *radically* ambivalent effects. With television or the computer, the polarization process not only occurs at more levels of involvement but tends to be less visible. Television programming, for example, is accused of filling minds with tripe even as it provides new and broader experiences for those watching it. Are the moral effects of television negligible or so pronounced in each direction as to create an ambivalence that makes these effects *appear* negligible? On moral, social, psychological, and economic levels the new technologies will not only breed their own evils, but counter those with new benefits. The precise effects of this technological schizophrenia have yet to be elaborated.

ENVIRONMENTS OVERLAP. In the Arctic, an ice cap forms on level land by the gradual accretion of new layers. The layers tend to give the cap shape and pronounced discrepancies in weight. Once its weight becomes pronounced, the cap or part of it breaks free and moves slowly, following its heaviest side, becoming a glacier. Technologies work much the way ice caps do, in that new accretions lead eventually to a threshold, after which the whole structure moves in the direction of the recent accretions.

In the conglomerate thought of these figures, not only do the environments overlap, but the ideas of what constitutes environmental accretion overlap as well. Mumford views the three great ages of modern technics as "phases," meaning that the new technologies have not simply displaced the old ones, but added to them, becoming a new vanguard. Giedion shows how early stages in mechanization built largely upon old methods, even when newer techniques were available. McLuhan uses the analogy of overlay maps: the new environment, when placed over the old ones, reveals patterns and trends within the other environments. Television, for example, makes us conscious of the movie as an environment. Fuller considers technological evolution as an almost direct thrust toward increased utilization of all available energy at the least cost. Technologies overlap only to the extent that dead political or economic ideas still function.

Nonetheless, the function of environmental overlap is important in all these men, as it suggests one of the critical patterns about technological growth and the significance of technology in society. We never live in the age of a new technology ("the age of automation," "the age of space," "the age of electronics"), but in the age of a new *vanguard* technology. The distinction is a vital one, and it can keep environmental thought from expecting too many shifting patterns immediately in the wake of a new innovation. The question is to what extent the vanguard technology alters our experience and interactions with the older, encrusted technologies.

WHAT CHANGES AND WHAT PERSISTS? "Over those who step into the same rivers," wrote Heraclitus five centuries before Christ, "different and ever different waters flow down." The question is one of the oldest known to man, and modern science, with its relativity theory and new knowledge of an expanding but dated universe, has only helped to raise it anew. In an age where technological change seems to threaten even the most buttressed institutions, the problem takes on grave importance. The question, and some tentative searches for an answer, undergirds the thought of each of these theorists.

Mumford views change against a persisting pattern: almost as a gestalt field-ground relationship. Culture and its values provide not only a firmament for the new technics, but a humanly based counterpoint as well. Mumford instinctively senses danger in change; it is too abrasive, values break free of their settled encrustations too easily; man is thrown by the whim of the moment. Little wonder that in *Technics and Civi-*

lization Mumford emphasizes persistence over change, and argues pointedly in *The Myth of the Machine* against an interpretation of history that assumes major changes on the part of human society and the human personality.

In *Mechanization Takes Command*, Siegfried Giedion views change within the larger pattern of organic continuity. Chairs and chair styles change, he says, but not the human need to sit down. Yet in leading deep into the twentieth century, Giedion suggests that reciprocal changes fostered by the new technologists may indeed be taking place; the design of low modern chairs, for example, has led to unaccustomed postures. Nonetheless, man's organic structure and his basic organic needs provide a basis for persistence amid the turmoil of technological change.

The question of persistence and change has significance for Ellul only within the context of his polemic against technique. Technique changes man, Ellul claims, largely by ingraining itself into his personality and life style. Ellul emphasizes the change to such an extent as to make it seem an invisible metanoia—a total transformation of society and personality. After such change the major principle of persistence becomes technique itself.

Harold Innis never approached the problem of persistence and change head-on, but his later writings are replete with ideas bordering on the problem. To him, cultures are information systems, with the important pattern of persistence being the information flow. What changes are those media that channel this flow. When a new medium such as television is introduced into a culture, it changes the latter's institutional structures, but not the essential definition of culture—the flow of information between economic, political, and religious institutions.

No one in this book suggests a more total concept of change than Marshall McLuhan. Not only does change become the norm in his work, but he offers scant suggestions as to its final ambits. In *Process and Reality,* Alfred North Whitehead recommends that persistence must be found *within* the patterns of change. McLuhan follows this recommendation in his theory of old environments becoming the content of the new environments: only through such patterns of change can we glimpse any final principle of continuity.

For Buckminster Fuller the problem is not too *much* change, but too little. Fuller is the only thinker in this volume to work from a basic theory of energetics, or nonsubstantial concepts. His thought shrugs off the problem of persistence and change, possibly postdating it. If a pattern of persistence had to be found in Fuller, his idea of natural patterns (geodesic, dymaxion, etc.) that can be located and utilized would serve.

There is no easy agreement among these men on the problem of change, only the near-unanimous recognition of it. If anything, it is clear that technology gives the problem new dimensions and fresh urgency.

COMMUNICATION IS ENVIRONMENTAL. One of the important concepts introduced by Innis, McLuhan, and their forebears is the environmental nature of communication. Is television essentially a medium of communications or an environmental phenomenon? The distinction gives way to a new recognition of the implicitly environmental action of media. Innis probed deep into the recesses of Western history to emphasize the environmental nature (while never using the word) of the communications media from the clay tablet to the Hearst newspaper. McLuhan gave added ramification to the equation by stressing the environmental and perceptual impact of a new medium over its "content" or information. Wiener and Fuller both emphasize that the very information that organized and unites modern culture tends to be environmental in its final effects. What is most important is that these men are not extending the concept of environment to include information and media, but that they are explicating the modern uses of information and media in such a way that their environmental character becomes evident.

WHAT A TECHNOLOGY IS AND WHAT IT DOES. A speculation: if these men had all been trained as engineers and technicians, how substantially different would their interpretations of the new environments be? Perhaps more than anything else, they would have looked for the continuity between the *structure* of a technology and its effects. Have the men treated in this book done so?

Emphatically. Mumford sees the use of wood as the structural material in early technics resulting in the conservative attitude of society toward the land. Giedion's central argument is that the *nature* of mechanization—its clockwork time, its economic use of space, its functional transformation of materials—provides the guiding clues to the effects of technology in society. Ellul's technique emerges from the machine and as its basic principle becomes the guiding force in life. Innis stresses the importance of a new medium's structure as the central shaping force for a temporal or spatial bias in the culture, with vast ramifications for institutions and beliefs. McLuhan has made the critical distinction between mechanical and electronic environments, not simply in their structural differences, but in the organs and organic functions that they extend. Wiener sees the basic function of the computer, information control, at the basis for stability and effective communication within a culture. A major axiom in Fuller's work is that there is no real distinction between the macrocosm and the microcosm, except as we perceive that difference with our unaided senses. For him, the patterns of nature are not only the patterns of life, but the guiding forces for technology as well.

One of the major distinctions made by these men is their attentiveness to the relationship between the structure of a technology and its effects. Too many studies of technological effects by economists and sociologists have ignored that balance of cause and effect, and their conclusions, revealing little of the inner workings of technology, have shown the failure to reach any major conclusions.

THE AMBITS OF TECHNOLOGICAL DETERMINISM. The theme of determinism has been a frequent one in this book, and perhaps it is the single most important question raised by the new environments. Virtually none of these thinkers agree with the commonplace that technology is morally neutral, that everything depends on man's control. If anything, all of them suggest some dimension of technology where control is impossible or futile.

These figures can be seen in three schools on the question of determinism. Mumford, Giedion, Ellul, and Wiener represent varying positions in the "Encroachment of the Machine" school. Innis and McLuhan suggest a principle of determinism that has already been called the "Media Dictates Culture" school. Fuller's determinism belongs in a class by itself, a kind of space-age Manifest Destiny, or the "Technology Breeds Utopia" school. In each case the level of determinism is pronounced; what differs are the values attached to each school.

The "Encroachment of the Machine" school has been discussed at some length in Chapter Two, "Golem Awakens." The machine is feared because it introduces principles alien to organic life, and those principles tend to grow and even "feed on" organic life. Ellul and Wiener both go as far as to give these principles an autonomous character, suggesting that we have passed or will pass the threshold of possible control. Mumford thinks control still possible, but unlikely.

The "Media Dictates Culture" school proposes an altogether different form of determinism; one that is inclusive of man rather than set over against him. Though using different routes of interpretation, Innis and McLuhan argue that the dominant media in a culture tend to restructure the institutions of the culture and the personalities it forms. These tendencies, while apparent enough in history, are difficult, perhaps impossible, to anticipate. To that extent, control is impossible as long as technologies mushroom. Curiously, while Innis and McLuhan refrain from attaching value assumptions to their determinism, it is a more extensive and thorough form than that proposed by Mumford, Giedion, or Fuller.

Fuller's implied slogan, "Technology Breeds Utopia," means that we have nothing to fear from technology but that anachronistic response, fear itself. Fuller is so sanguine that his determinism hardly appears to be a determinism at all, but a promise of technological cornucopia.

It is true that any major theory of the technological environment would be, almost by definition, deterministic to some extent. The questions raised by these men in their determinism are: What can man do? How can he at least become conscious of the controls that technology has placed on him? And can he, or should he, look for some means of overcoming these controls?

The preceding twelve postulates offer only the most basic and tentative steps toward a deeper exploration of man's relationship to his new environment. They serve little more than as a summary of junctures of thought among the most pronounced theorists in this area today. But they may help overcome the danger that arises in the early stages of any new terrain of thought, the adherence of dogmatic disciples to the tentative ideas of a major thinker. "To the founder of a school," quipped Albert Guérard in *Literature and Society*, "everything may be forgiven, except his school." When the questions are as large and urgent as those raised by Mumford, Ellul, McLuhan, Wiener, and Fuller, it would be lamentable to see those seeking to answer them fragmented into schools of strict "McLuhanites," "Ellulians," and "Fullerites." Hopefully the day has passed when a discipline must achieve early codification and a canonical fidelity to a single method. Man's total relationship to the environment he has shaped and misshaped should remain a question long before it becomes ossified into an answer.

Bibliography

Ackoff, R. L., "Games, Decisions and Organizations," *General Systems* (1959), 145-150.

Adams, Henry, *The Education of Henry Adams*, Boston: Houghton Mifflin, 1961.

———, *Mont-Saint-Michel and Chartres*, New York: New American Library, 1961.

Arnheim, Rudolf, *Art and Visual Perception*, Berkeley: University of California Press, 1966.

———, *Toward a Psychology of Art*, Berkeley: University of California Press, 1967.

Arnold, Matthew, *Culture and Anarchy*, ed. J. Dover Wilson, London: Cambridge University Press, 1966.

Bacon, Francis, "The New Atlantis," in *Essays, Civil and Moral*, Vol. 3, New York: Herald Classics, P. F. Collier & Sons, 1903.

Bekesy, George von, *Experiments in Hearing*, ed. and trans. E. G. Weber, New York: McGraw Hill, 1960.

Bellamy, Edward, *Looking Backward*, New York: New American Library, 1964.

Bergson, Henri, *Time and Free Will*, New York: Harper Bros., 1960.

Berkeley, George, *A New Theory of Vision and Other Writings*, New York: E. P. Dutton, 1922.

Bertalanffy, Ludwig von, *Robots, Men and Minds*, New York: George Braziller, 1967.

Boas, Franz, *The Mind of Primitive Man*, New York: Macmillan, 1938.

Boguslaw, Robert, *The New Utopians*, Englewood Cliffs, N.J.: Prentice-Hall, 1965.

Boorstin, Daniel J., *The Image: A Guide to Pseudo-Events in America*, New York: Harper & Row, 1964.

Born, Max, *Einstein's Theory of Relativity*, New York: Dover, 1962.

Boulding, Kenneth E., *The Image*, Ann Arbor, Mich.: The University of Michigan Press, 1966.

Brown, Norman O., *Life Against Death, The Psychoanalytical Meaning of History*, New York: Vintage Books, 1959.

Burckhardt, Jacob, *Force and Freedom*, New York: Meridian Books, 1955.

Butler, Samuel, *Erewhon and Erewhon Revisited*, New York: Random House (Modern Library), 1955.

Calder, Nigel (ed.), *The World in 1984*, Vol. 1, Baltimore: Penguin Books, 1965.

Calder, Ritchie, *The Evolution of the Machine*, New York: American Heritage, 1968.

Čapek, Milic, *Philosophical Impact of Contemporary Physics*, Princeton, N.J.: D. Van Nostrand, 1961.

Carpenter, Edmund; Varley, Frederick; and Flaherty, Robert; *Eskimo*, Toronto: University of Toronto Press, 1964.

Cassirer, Ernst, *An Essay on Man*, New Haven, Conn.: Yale University Press, 1966.

———, *Language and Myth*, trans. Susanne K. Langer, New York: Harper & Row, 1965.

Chardin, Pierre Teilhard de, *The Phenomenon of Man*, New York: Harper & Row, 1965.

Cherry, Colin, *On Human Communication*, Cambridge, Mass.: M.I.T. Press, 1966.

Dantzig, Robias, *Number. The Language of Science*, Garden City, N.Y.: Doubleday, 1954.

Dechert, Charles R. (ed.), *The Social Impact of Cybernetics*, Notre Dame: University of Notre Dame Press, 1966.

Dember, William N., *Psychology of Perception*, New York: Holt, Rinehart & Winston, 1966.

Ellul, Jacques, *A Critique of the New Commonplace*, trans. Helen Weaver, New York: Alfred A. Knopf, 1968.

———, *The Political Illusion*, trans. Konrad Keller, New York: Alfred A. Knopf, 1967.

———, *The Presence of the Kingdom*, trans. Olive Wyon, Philadelphia: Westminster Press, 1951.

———, *Propaganda: The Formation of Men's Attitudes*, New York: Alfred A. Knopf, 1968.

———, *The Technological Order*, ed. Carl F. Stover, Proceedings of the Encyclopaedia Britannica Conference, Detroit: Wayne State University Press, 1963.

———, *The Technological Society*, trans. John Wilkison, New York: Alfred A. Knopf, 1965.

Elynes, Manfred and Kline, Nathan S., "Cyborgs and Space," *Astronautics* (September 1960), 27.

Fabun, Don, *The Dynamics of Change*, Englewood Cliffs, N.J.: Prentice-Hall, 1968.

Ferkiss, Victor C., *Technological Man: The Myth and the Reality*, New York: George Braziller, 1969.

Fink, Donald G., *Computers and the Human Mind*, New York: Doubleday, 1966.

Finkelstein, Sidney, *Sense and Nonsense of McLuhan*, New York: International, 1968.

Fuller, R. Buckminster, "The Age of Astro-Architecture," *Saturday Review* (July 13, 1968), 17-19 ff.

———, *Education Automation*, Carbondale, Ill.: Southern Illinois University Press, 1962.

———, *Ideas and Integrities*, ed. Robert W. Marks, Englewood Cliffs, N.J.: Prentice-Hall, 1963.

———, "Man with a Chronofile," *Saturday Review* (April 1, 1967), 14-18.

———, *Nine Chains to the Moon*, Carbondale, Ill.: Southern Illinois University Press, 1963.

———, *No More Secondhand God and other writings*, Carbondale, Ill.: Southern Illinois University Press, 1963.

———, *Operating Manual for Spaceship Earth*, Carbondale, Ill.: Southern Illinois University Press, 1969.

———, "Report on the 'Geosocial Revolution,' " *Saturday Review* (September 16, 1967), 31-33 ff.

———, *Untitled Epic Poem on the History of Industrialization*, Charlotte, N.C.: Heritage, 1962.

———, *Utopia or Oblivion: The Prospects for Humanity,* New York: Bantam Books, 1969.

———, "Vision 65," *The American Scholar* (Spring 1966).

Fuller, Buckminster, and McHale, John, *World Design Science Decade 1965-1975,* Carbondale, Ill.: World Resources Inventory, 1963, 6 vols.

Furnas, J. C., *The Next Hundred Years,* Baltimore: Williams & Wilkins, 1936.

Furth, Hans G., *Thinking Without Language: Psychological Implications of Deafness,* New York: Free Press, 1968.

Gabor, Dennis, *Inventing the Future,* New York: Alfred A. Knopf, 1963.

Geddes, Patrick, *Cities in Evolution,* new rev. ed., New York: Oxford University Press, 1950.

———, *A Study in City Development,* London: Fort George Press, 1904.

Gibson, James J., *The Perception of the Visual World,* Cambridge, Mass.: Riverside Press, 1950.

Giedion, Siegfried, *The Eternal Present: The Beginnings of Architecture,* New York: Bollingen Foundation, 1964.

———, *Mechanization Takes Command,* New York: Oxford University Press, 1948.

———, *Space, Time and Architecture,* rev. and enl. ed., Cambridge, Mass.: Harvard University Press, 1967.

Gombrich, E. H., *Art and Illusion,* New York: Bollingen Foundation, 1965.

Grazia, Sebastian de, *Of Time, Work, and Leisure,* Garden City, N.Y.: Doubleday, 1964.

Halacy, D. S., Jr., *Cyborg–Evolution of the Superman,* New York: Harper & Row, 1965.

Hall, Edward T., *The Silent Language,* Greenwich Conn.: Fawcett, 1965.

———, *The Hidden Dimension,* New York: Doubleday and Company, 1966.

Hanika, F. P. de, *New Thinking in Management,* London: Hutchinson, 1965.

Havelock, Eric A., *Preface to Plato,* New York: Grosset & Dunlap, 1967.

Heilbroner, Robert L., *The Future as History*, New York: Grove Press, 1961.

Heisenberg, Werner, *The Physicist's Conception of Nature*, London: Hutchinson, 1958.

Helmer, Olaf, *Social Technology*, with contributions by Bernice Brown and Theodore Gordon, New York: Basic Books, 1966.

Huizinga, Johann, *Homo Ludens*, Boston: Beacon Press, 1964.

Huxley, Aldous, *Brave New World*, New York: Bantam Books, 1962.

———, *Brave New World Revisited*, New York: Bantam Books, 1960.

Innis, Harold A., *The Bias of Communication*, Toronto: University of Toronto Press, 1951.

———, *Empire and Communications*, London: Oxford University Press, 1950.

———, *Essays in Canadian Economic History*, Toronto: University of Toronto Press, 1956.

———, *The Fur Trade in Canada*, New Haven: Conn.: Yale University Press, 1930.

Ivins, William, Jr., *Art and Geometry: A Study in Space Limitations*, New York: Dover, 1946.

———, *Prints and Visual Communication*, London: Routledge & Kegan Paul, 1953.

Jouvenal, Bertrand de, *The Art of Conjecture*, New York: Basic Books, 1967.

Jünger, Friedrich Georg, *The Failure of Technology*, Chicago: Henry Regnery, 1956.

Jungk, Robert, *Tomorrow Is Already Here; Scenes from a Man-Made World*, London: Rupert Hart-Davis, 1954.

Kepes, Gyorgy (ed.), *Education of Vision*, New York: George Braziller, 1965.

———, *Language of Vision*, Chicago: Paul Theobald, 1964.

Koestler, Arthur, *The Ghost in the Machine*, New York: Macmillan, 1968.

Kahn, Herman, and Wiener, Anthony J., *The Year 2000: a Framework for Speculation on the Next Thirty-Three Years*, New York: Macmillan, 1967.

Kilpatrick, F. P., *Explorations in Transactional Psychology*, New York: New York University Press, 1961.

Kuhn, Thomas S., *The Structure of Scientific Revolutions*, Chicago: University of Chicago Press, 1967.

Kuhns, William, *Environmental Man*, New York: Harper & Row, 1969.

Laue, Theodore H. von, *The Global City*, Philadelphia, Pa.: J. B. Lippincott, 1969.

Lewis, Arthur O., Jr., *Of Men and Machines*, New York: E. P. Dutton, 1963.

Lewis, Wyndham, *The Lion and the Fox*, London: Great Richards Press, 1927.

———, *Time and Western Man*, Boston: Beacon Press, 1957.

Lifton, Robert Jay, *Thought Reform and the Psychology of Totalism*, New York: W. W. Norton, 1963.

Lowenthal, Leo, *Popular Culture and Society*, Englewood Cliffs, N.J.: Prentice-Hall, 1961.

Marcuse, Herbert, *One-Dimensional Man*, Boston: Beacon Press, 1966.

Marks, Robert W., *The Dymaxion World of Buckminster Fuller*, Carbondale, Ill.: Southern Illinois University Press, 1960.

McHale, John, *Buckminster Fuller*, New York: George Braziller, 1962.

———, *The Future of the Future*, New York: George Braziller, 1969.

McLuhan, Marshall, *Counterblast*, Toronto: McClelland & Stewart, 1966.

———, (ed.), *Explorations in Communications*, with E. S. Carpenter, Boston: Beacon Press, 1960.

———, *The Gutenberg Galaxy*, Toronto: University of Toronto Press, 1962.

———, "Interview with Playboy," *Playboy* (March 1969), 53-62 ff.

———, *The McLuhan Dew-Line*, New York: Human Development Corporation, 1968-1969, Vol. 1, nos. 1-12.

———, *The Mechanical Bride*, Boston: Beacon Press, 1951.

———, "Sight, Sound and Fury," in *Mass Culture: The Popular Arts in America*, eds. B. Rosenberg and D. M. White, Glencoe, Ill.: Free Press, 1967.

———, *Verbi-Voco-Visual Explorations*, New York: Something Else Press, 1967.

———, *Understanding Media: The Extensions of Man*, New York: McGraw-Hill, 1965.

McLuhan, Marshall, and Fiore, Quentin, *The Medium is the Massage*, New York: Bantam Books, 1967.

———, *War and Peace in the Global Village*, New York: Bantam Books, 1968.

McLuhan, Marshall, and Parker, Harley, *Through the Vanishing Point; Space in Poetry and Painting*, ed. Ruth Nanda Anshen, New York: Harper & Row, 1968.

Mills, C. Wright, *The Power Elite*, New York: Oxford University Press, 1959.

Mounier, Emanuel, *Be Not Afraid*, trans. Cynthia Rowland, New York: Sheed and Ward, 1962.

Mumford, Lewis, *Art and Technics*, New York: Columbia University Press, 1964.

———, *The City in History*, New York: Harcourt, Brace & World, 1961.

———, *The Condition of Man*, New York: Harcourt, Brace & World, 1944.

———, *The Conduct of Life*, New York: Harcourt, Brace & World, 1951.

———, *The Culture of Cities*, New York: Harcourt, Brace & World, 1938.

———, *From the Ground Up*, New York: Harcourt, Brace & World, 1956.

———, *The Highway and the City*, New York: Harcourt, Brace & World, 1964.

———, *The Myth of the Machine*, New York: Harcourt, Brace & World, 1966, 1967.

———, *The Story of Utopias*, New York: Viking Press, 1962.

———, *Technics and Civilization*, New York: Harcourt, Brace & World, 1963.

———, *The Transformations of Man*, New York: Collier Books, 1966.

———, *The Urban Prospect*, New York: Harcourt, Brace & World, 1968.

Neuman, John von, *The Computer and the Brain*, New Haven, Conn.: Yale University Press, 1964.

Ong, Walter J., S.J., *In the Human Grain*, New York: Macmillan, 1967.

———, (ed.), *Knowledge and the Future of Man, an International Symposium,* New York: Simon & Schuster, 1968.

———, *The Presence of the Word*, New Haven, Conn.: Yale University Press, 1967.

———, *Ramus, Method and the Decay of Dialogue*, Cambridge: Harvard University Press, 1958.

Ortega y Gasset, José, *The Revolt of the Masses*, New York: W. W. Norton, 1932.

Orwell, George, *1984*, New York: New American Library of World Literature, 1964.

Philipson, Morris, *Automation; Implications for the Future*, New York: Random House (Vintage Books), 1962.

Plato Dialogues, trans. Benjamin Jowett, New York: Oxford University Press, 1892.

Polak, Fred L., *The Image of the Future*, New York: Oceana, 1961, 2 vols.

Priestley, J. B., *Man and Time*, New York: Dell, 1968.

Rosenberg, B., and White, D. M. (eds.), *Mass Culture: The Popular Arts in America,* Glencoe, Ill.: Free Press, 1967.

Rosenthal, Raymond (ed.), *McLuhan: Pro and Con*, Baltimore: Penguin Books, 1969.

Russell, Bertrand, *ABC of Relativity*, New York: New American Library, 1959.

Sapir, Edward, *Language*, New York: Harcourt, Brace & World, 1949.

Saveth, Edward N. (ed.), *Henry Adams*, New York: Washington Square Press, 1963.

Searles, Harold F., *The Nonhuman Environment*, New York: International Universities Press, 1960.

Seidenberg, Roderick, *Post-Historic Man*; *an Inquiry*, Boston: Beacon Press, 1957.

Sharpe, Mitchell R., *Living in Space*, New York: Doubleday, 1969.
Skinner, B. F., *Walden Two*, New York: Macmillan, 1967.
Stearn, Julian H., *McLuhan: Hot and Cold*, New York: Dial Press, 1967.
Steward, Julian H., *Theory of Culture Change: The Methodology of Multi-linear Evolution*, Urbana, Ill.: University of Illinois Press, 1955.
Stover, Carl F. (ed.), *The Technological Order*, Proceedings of the Encyclopaedia Britannica Conference, Detroit: Wayne State University Press, 1963.
Swartz, Robert J. (ed.), *Perceiving, Sensing, and Knowing*, New York, 1965.
Toffles, Alvin, *Future Shock*, New York: Random House, 1970.
Vernon, M. D. (ed.), *Experiments in Visual Perception*, Baltimore: Penguin Books, 1966.
———, *The Psychology of Perception*, Baltimore: Penguin Books, 1966.
Whitehead, Alfred North, *Adventures of Ideas*, New York: Free Press, 1967.
———, *Process and Reality*, New York: Harper & Row, 1960.
———, *Science and the Modern World*, New York: Free Press, 1967.
Whorf, Benjamin Lee, *Language, Thought and Reality*, ed. John B. Carroll, Cambridge, Mass.: M.I.T. Press,
Wiener, Norbert, *Cybernetics or Control and Communication in the Animal and the Machine*, Cambridge, Mass.: M.I.T. Press, 1965.
———, *Ex-Prodigy*, Cambridge, Mass.: M.I.T. Press, 1966, 2 vols.
———, *God and Golem, Inc.*, Cambridge, Mass.: M.I.T. Press, 1966.
———, *The Human Use of Human Beings*, Garden City, N.Y.: Doubleday, 1954.
———, *I am a Mathematician; The Later Life of a Prodigy*, Cambridge, Mass.: M.I.T. Press, 1966, vol. 2.
———, "Some Moral and Technical Consequences of Automation,"
Science, 131 (May 6, 1960), 1355-1359, also in Morris Philipson, *Automation; Implications for the Future*, New York: Random House (Vintage Books), 1962.
———, *Medieval Technology and Social Change*, London: Oxford University Press, 1967.

Notes

The quotes on p. 17 are from Karel Čapek, *R.U.R.*, in Arthur O. Lewis, Jr., *Of Men and Machines* (New York: Dutton, 1963), pp. 8, 9, 58.

The quotes from Samuel Butler, "Darwin Among the Machines," on pp. 22 and 23 are from Arthur O. Lewis, Jr., *Of Men and Machines* (New York: Dutton, 1963), pp. 183, 185.

The quote from Norbert Wiener on p. 23 is from *The Human Use of Human Beings* (Garden City, N.Y.: Doubleday, 1954), p. 32.

The quote from Roderick Seidenberg on p. 24 is from *Post-Historic Man; an Inquiry* (Boston: Beacon, 1957), p. 113.

The quote from Friedrich Jünger on p. 25 is from *The Failure of Technology* (Chicago: Henry Regnery, 1956), p. xi.

The epigraph on p. 32 is from Lewis Mumford, *Art and Technics* (New York: Columbia University Press, 1964), pp. 11-12.

The extract on p. 37 is from Lewis Mumford, *The Story of Utopias* (New York: Viking, 1962), p. 4.

The quote on p. 53 is from Lewis Mumford, *The Myth of the Machine* (New York: Harcourt, Brace & World, 1966), p. 3.

The Giedion quotations in Chapter Four are from *Mechanization Takes Command* (New York: Oxford University Press, 1948).

The Ellul quotations in Chapter Five are from *The Technological Order* (Detroit: Wayne State University Press, 1963), *The Technological Society* (New York: Knopf, 1965), and *Propaganda: The Formation of Men's Attitudes* (New York: Knopf, 1968).

The quote from Edward Hall on p. 126 is from *The Silent Language* (Greenwich, Conn.: Fawcett, 1965), p. 113.

The quote on p. 130 is from Siegfried Giedion, *The Eternal Present: The Beginnings of Art and Architecture* (New York: Bollingen Foundation, 1964), p. 528.

The quote on p. 131 is from William Irvins, Jr., *Art and Geometry: A Study in Space Limitations* (New York: Dover, 1946), p. 16.

The quote on p. 135 is from Walter Ong, S.J., *Ramus: Method and the Decay of Dialogue* (Cambridge: Harvard University Press, 1958), pp. 89-90.

The quote on p. 136 is from Walter Ong, S.J., *The Presence of the Word* (New Haven, Conn.: Yale University Press, 1967), p. 89.

The epigraph on p. 139 is from H. A. Innis, *The Bias of Communication* (Toronto: University of Toronto Press, 1956), p. 34.

The Innis quotations in Chapter Seven are from *The Bias of Communication* (Toronto: University of Toronto Press, 1956) and *Empire and Communications* (London: Oxford University Press, 1950).

The McLuhan quote on pp. 166-167 is from *The Gutenberg Galaxy* (Toronto: University of Toronto Press, 1962), p. 216.

The McLuhan quotations in Chapter Eight are from *Understanding Media: The Extensions of Man* (New York: McGraw-Hill, 1965), *The Gutenberg Galaxy* (Toronto: University of Toronto Press, 1962), and an interview with *Playboy* magazine, *Playboy* (March 1969).

The epigraph on p. 220 is from R. Buckminster Fuller, *Utopia or Oblivion: The Prospects for Humanity* (New York: Bantam, 1969), p. 1.

The Fuller quote on p. 222 is from Robert W. Marks, *The Dymaxion World of Buckminster Fuller* (Carbondale, Ill.: Southern Illinois University Press, 1960), p. 63.

The quote on p. 227 is from R. Buckminster Fuller, *Operating Manual for Spaceship Earth* (Carbondale, Ill.: Southern Illinois University Press, 1969), p. 9.

The quote on pp. 233-234 is from R. Buckminster Fuller, *Ideas and Integrities* (Englewood Cliffs, N.J.: Prentice-Hall, 1963), pp. 75-76.

The epigraph on p. 247 is from Don Fabun, *The Dynamics of Change* (Englewood Cliffs, N.J.: Prentice-Hall, 1968), p. 12.

Index

73 74 75 12 11 10 9 8 7 6 5 4 3 2 1